Maths skills

Shirley Clarke & Barry Silsby

Illustrated by Sascha Lipscomb

Headway • Hodder & Stoughton

NOTES FOR PARENTS

Research has shown that when children and parents work together at home, the child's work at school improves.

The purpose of the *Headstart* books is to provide activities which your child will enjoy doing and which will encourage learning to take place in the home.

Each of the activities in this book is linked to one or more of the Attainment Targets of the Maths National Curriculum. (See the chart on p. 32.)

You can help your child get the most out of this book by:

- *talking about the activities,* without 'telling' your child how to do them. Encourage your child to think of different ways of working things out.
- *reading the advice below.* This gives further information and explains the purpose of each activity.
- *letting your child control the pace* of working through the book. Too many pages in one go may put your child off.
- *giving lots of praise and encouragement.* Children get better at subjects they believe they are good at.

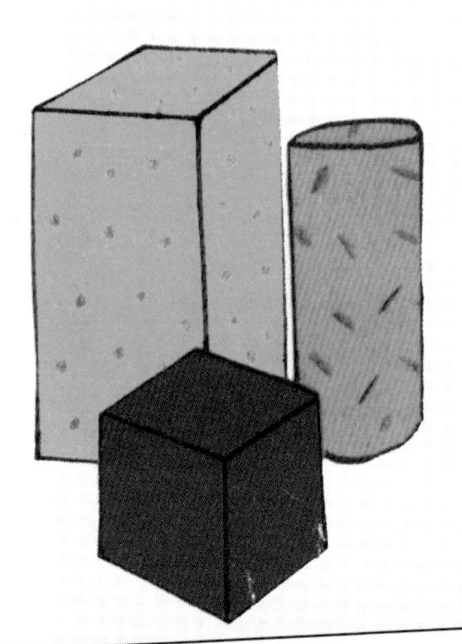

Pages 4 – 5 Shape experiment

By physically handling 3D shapes, your child can take time to count faces and edges ('sides' apply to 2D shapes only). By rolling and stacking the shapes your child is finding out more about them, which will lead to an appreciation of why certain shapes are used in different environments such as industry.

Pages 6 – 7 Do you agree?

This activity is meant to be a fun means of collecting and interpreting data. Some of the statements (like 'hunting is cruel') could lead to interesting discussions amongst the members of your family. Other statements (like 'the tooth fairy does not leave enough money') will prompt fairly predictable responses, depending on whether a child or an adult is being asked the question. It is important that your child feels in control of the data he or she has gathered. Encourage him or her to draw conclusions from it (for example, maybe more help could be given around the house).

Pages 8 – 9 Symmetry grids

This activity introduces patterns with two lines of symmetry, where your child has an active role in 'creating' symmetrical patterns. Encourage your child to colour the grids in faintly at first, in case of mistakes, so that they can be rubbed out easily.

Pages 10 – 11 Treasure hunt

This game aims to help your child learn the directions of the compass points: north, south, east and west. The grid can be used again and again, with different treasure hunts.

Pages 12 – 13 Will it, won't it?

This fun activity will help your child with the notion of probability, and will cause a few laughs!

Pages 14 – 15 Sort it out

Children are often asked to sort shapes, but this activity asks them to decide how someone else has sorted the shapes on the page. You may need to talk through the activity with your child, until he or she grasps the idea of identifying properties. Ask questions like, 'What is the same about all of these shapes?' and, 'In what way are all of these shapes different from all of these?'

Pages 16 – 17 Headstart quiz

These questions aim to do more than just test general maths knowledge. Some of the answers will provide new information for your child.

Pages 18 – 19 Don't be a litterbug!

This game aims to teach children the directions of the compass points. It also has the potential for encouraging some strategic thinking, as the choice of starting place is important if you do not want to miss too many goes. As two of the compass points have been left out (because a dice has only six faces), you could swap them in to vary the games you play.

Pages 20 – 21 Decisions, decisions

This activity will encourage your child to make decisions about probability. The need for some objects will depend on your circumstances (for example, if you always go to the swimming pool in the car, you probably won't need the bike). In any cases of this kind, the statement will have to go in the middle column.

Pages 22 – 23 Going shopping

This activity involves two things: completing a graph from the given information in the book, and then constructing a graph after collecting some information. Your child can collect this information in two ways: either by asking, 'What is your favourite fruit?' or by asking, 'What is your favourite fruit out of these - apple, orange, banana or pear ?' (or a similar limited list). Either way will produce interesting results.

Pages 24 – 25 Symmetry search

Symmetry exists all around us, not just in maths. The Alhambra Palace tile patterns are famous for their geometric beauty. This activity aims to help your child identify several lines of symmetry, and also appreciate the beauty of geometric mathematics. Use a small mirror to help you check that your child has put the lines in the right place.

Pages 26 – 27 Time off

This spread involves interpreting data from a timetable.

Pages 28 – 29 Family favourites

The object of data handling and surveys is to be able to interpret the results for a particular purpose. The purpose of this survey is to look for similarities and differences in the preferences of males and females. If there are no patterns in the data your child obtains (because every one in the family gives a different response), suggest that he or she asks the family to choose their favourite meal, colour etc. from a list of four.

Pages 30 – 31 Database

Accessing information from a database involves finding out new things from a set of statistics. The data in this spread tells us which clubs are most popular for boys and girls, and whether the day of the week affects attendance at the clubs.

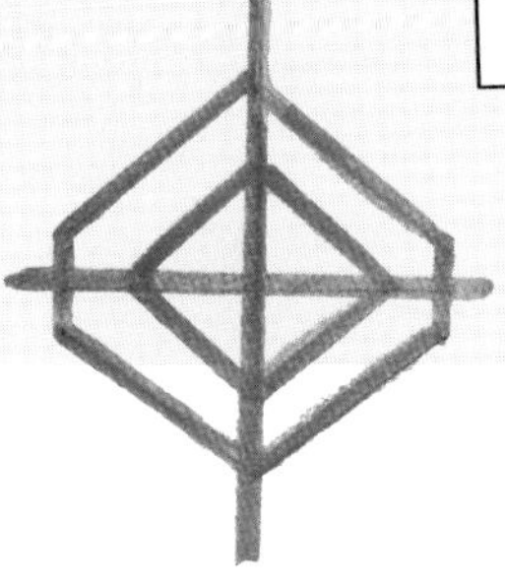

Shape experiment

Find some of these shapes in your home.

cubes

(such as square boxes or stock cubes)

cuboids

(such as long boxes or cereal packets)

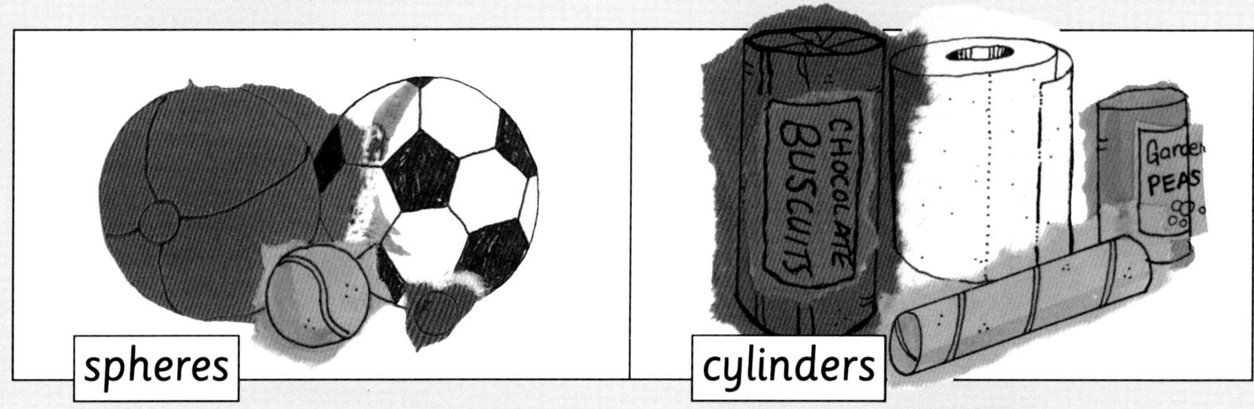

spheres

(such as tennis balls or footballs)

cylinders

(such as kitchen rolls or toilet roll centres)

Now try these experiments with your shapes.

1 Find out which shapes **roll.** Tick (✔) those that **do.**

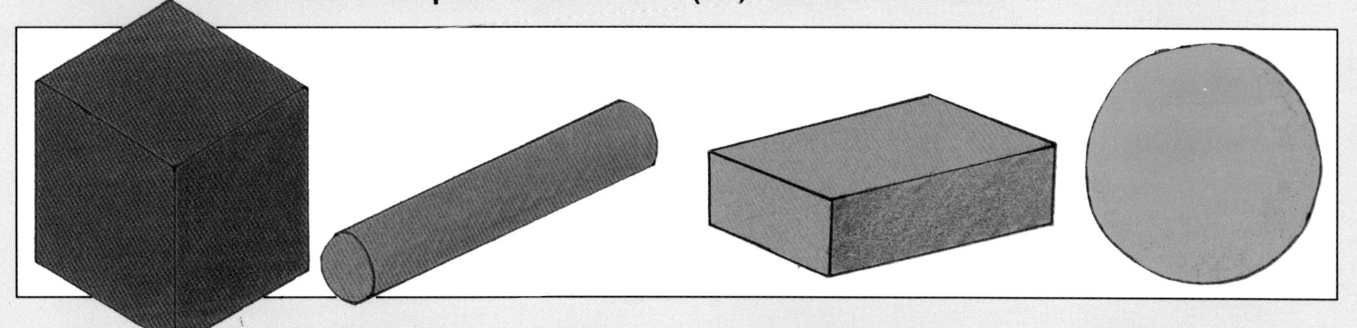

2 Find out which shapes **stack.** Tick (✔) those that **do.**

3 Find out which shapes have **six faces.** Tick (✔) those that **do.**

4 Find out which shapes have **two edges or less.** Tick (✔) those that **do.**

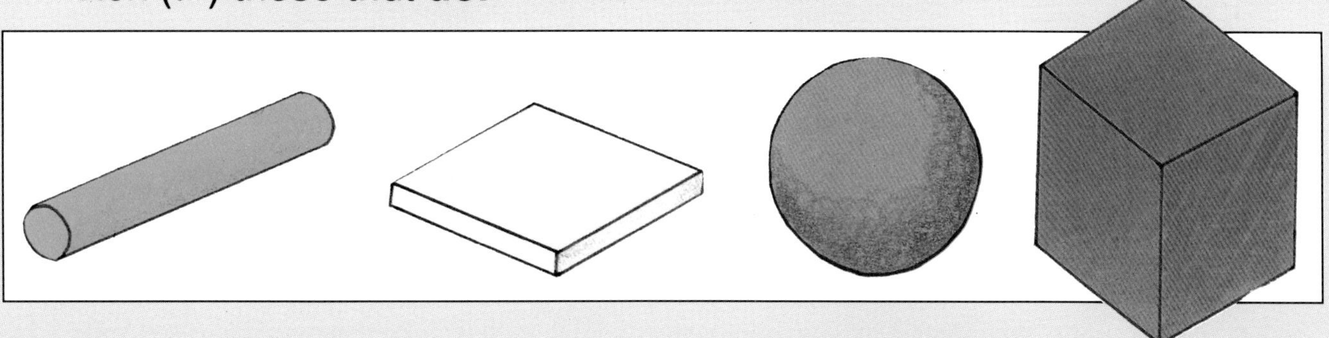

Now find out something about the shapes for yourself.

I have ticked those shapes which

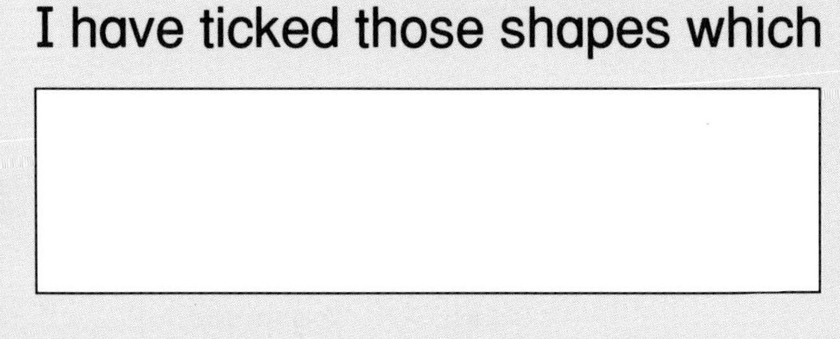

Do you agree?

How well do you, your family and your friends agree with one another? Here's a survey to find out!

1 First decide whether *you* agree or disagree with each of the statements on the opposite page. Fill in one of the columns of the chart with your answers.	**2** Now ask some of your family and friends whether they agree or disagree with the statements. Fill in their answers on the chart. Put a ✔ if they agree and a ✘ if they disagree.	**3** Count how many people agreed and how many people disagreed with each statement. Write the number in the total column.

Now answer these questions:

- Are there any statements you all agree with? ______________
- Are there any statements you all disagree with? ___________
- Are there any statements that all the adults agree with and all the children disagree with? ______________________________
- Are there any statements that all the children agree with and all the adults disagree with? ____________________________

	Name		Name		Name		Name		Name		Name		Name		TOTAL	
	✔	✘	✔	✘	✔	✘	✔	✘	✔	✘	✔	✘	✔	✘	✔	✘
Hunting is cruel.																
It is better to feel too hot than too cold.																
Television is good for you.																
Cabbage is disgusting.																
Pets are a nuisance.																
To get rid of hiccups, hold your breath.																
Counting goes on forever.																
Holidays are fun.																
The tooth fairy doesn't leave enough money.																
Children should help around the home.																

Symmetry grids

Colour in the other half of this grid to make a symmetrical pattern. Use exactly the same colours as in the book.

The line down the middle of the grid is called a **line of symmetry.**

Now colour in this grid where the line of symmetry is in a different place.

This pattern has two lines of symmetry.

Look carefully at how the pattern is symmetrical in two ways.

Now colour in these patterns with two lines of symmetry.

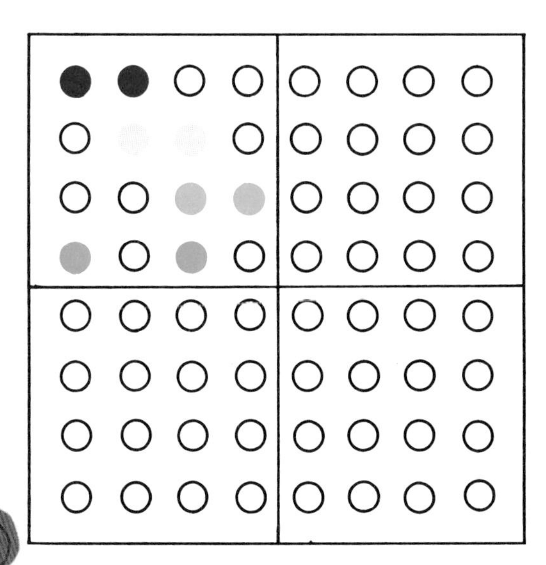

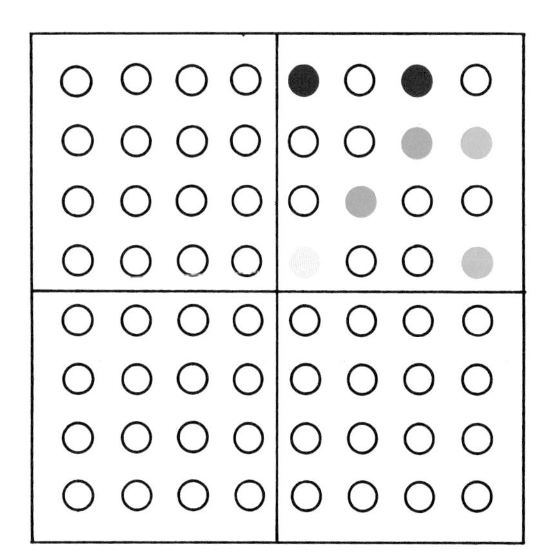

You might find it easier if you turn the book around as you go!

Use this grid to make a symmetrical pattern of your own. Draw in your pattern's lines of symmetry.

Treasure hunt

Follow the route to find the treasure!

Put a counter on start and follow the instructions.
(The compass will help you.)

Find out which square the treasure is hidden in.

1 Go N 3 squares.
2 Go E 4 squares.
3 Go N 1 square.
4 Go W 2 squares.
5 Go S 4 squares.
6 Go E 2 squares.
7 Go N 6 squares.
8 Go W 3 squares.

The treasure is in square number ☐

Now try this different treasure hunt:

1 Go E 4 squares.
2 Go N 1 square.
3 Go W 2 squares.
4 Go N 3 squares.
5 Go W 1 square.
6 Go E 3 squares.
7 Go N 2 squares.
8 Go S 4 squares.

The treasure is in square number ☐

Answers on page 32.

Why not make up your own treasure hunt and ask your family or friends to solve it?

Will it, won't it?

Decide whether each of these statements:

- is impossible
- might happen
- is certain

Draw a line from each statement to the right box.

A six month old will win the high jump competition in the Olympics.

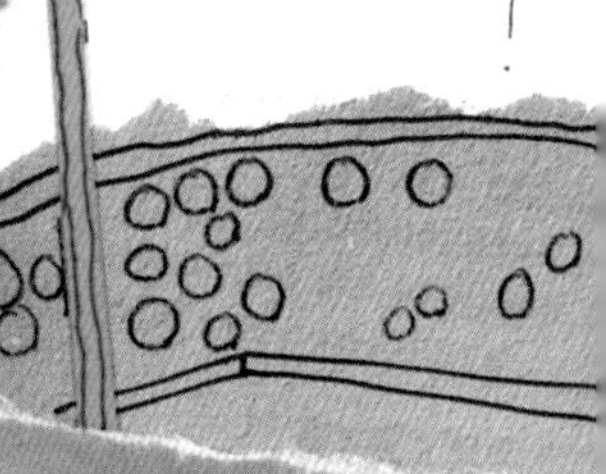

Someone in the world will be born on the same day as me.

My mum will meet the Queen of England.

Rabbits will all lose their tails tomorrow.

I shall be famous one day.

It will rain every day for six weeks.
2 is more than 1.
I shall grow up to be a frog.
I woke up this morning.
might happen
is certain
I shall double my age in two years
The next Disneyland will be built on the moon.

Sort it out

These robots sort shapes in different ways. They have created a shape challenge for you.

Look carefully at the shapes below and see if you can find out how they sorted these shapes.

They are sorted into shapes which have 3 sides and shapes which do not have 3 sides. (**Or**: shapes which are triangles and shapes which are not triangles.)

Now try these robot shape challenges!

1

do have	do not have

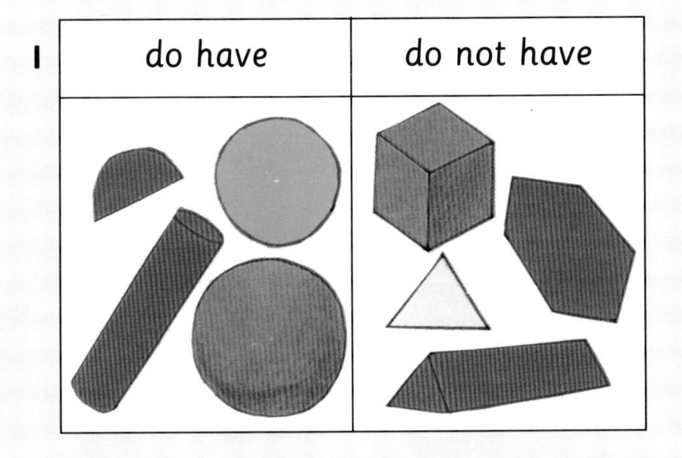

2

do have	do not have

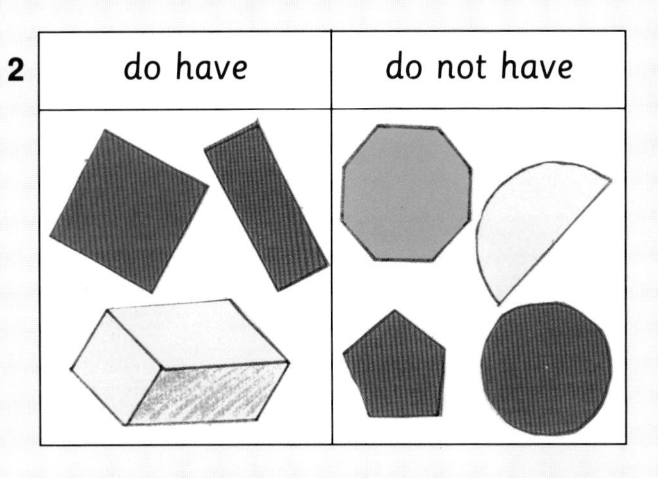

3

do have	do not have

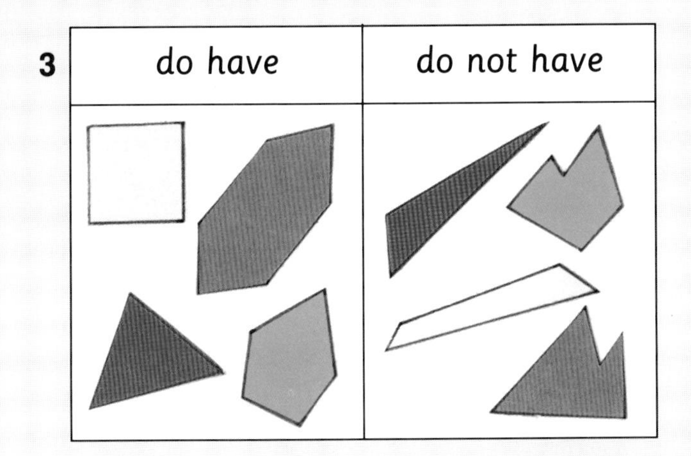

Make one up of your own here:

4

do have	do not have

Headstart quiz

How many of the questions can you answer?

HEADStart

What is the total number of sides in one triangle, two hexagons and three squares?

6

HEADStart

Is your body symmetrical?

7

HEADStart

What shape is a cereal box?

8

HEADStart

If two dice are thrown and the numbers added, what is the most likely total?

9

HEADStart

What shape do you get in the middle of a five pointed star if you join the inside corners together?

10

Answers on Page 32

Don't be a litterbug!

Here's a game for two or more people to play.
The playground is full of rubbish which needs picking up.

You need

10 small pieces of scrunched-up paper (smaller than the squares opposite).
A counter for each player. A die.

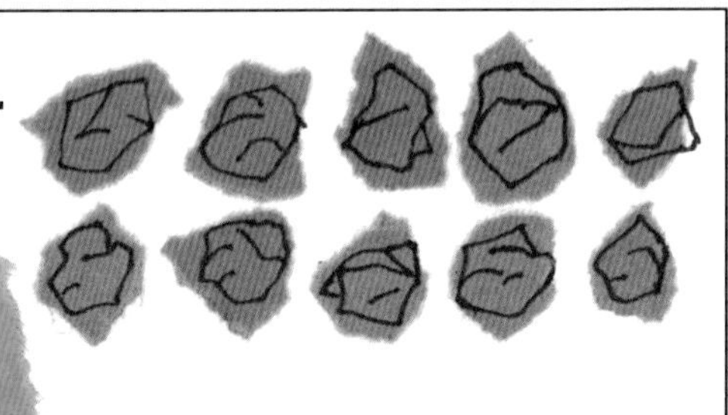

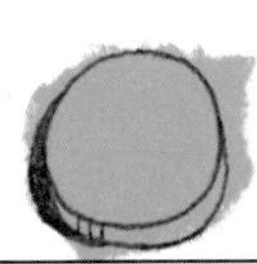

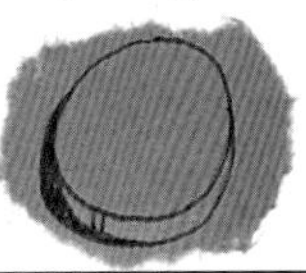

How to play:

- Place the scraps of paper on ten squares of your choice.
- Choose where you want to put your counter to start.
- Throwing the die, move your counter as shown opposite.
- Pick up any paper in any square you land on.
- The first player to pick up five pieces of paper is the winner.
- If you can't move, miss a go.

This compass will help you.

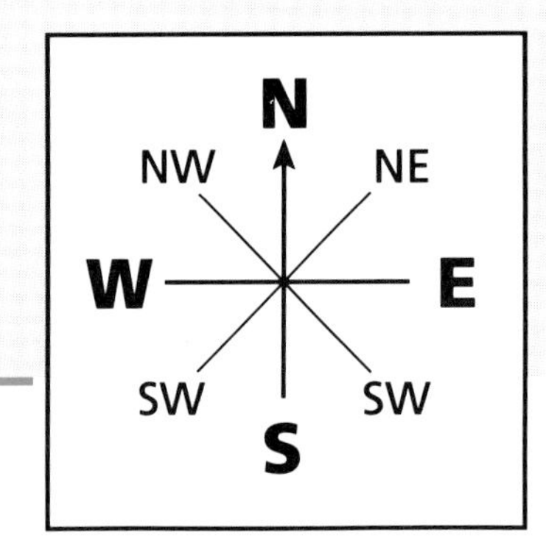

How to move

Die	Move
1	Go N one square
2	Go S one square
3	Go SE one square
4	Go E one square
5	Go W one square
6	Go NW one square

Play this game several times. Where is the best place to start so you don't have to miss too many goes?

Decisions, decisions

Imagine you are going swimming. Which of the things in the picture opposite would you:

- definitely need;
- possibly need;
- definitely not need?

Write the name of each item in the correct column below.

definitely need	possibly need	definitely not need

Has anything been left out of the lists?
If you can think of anything else, write it in.

front door key
shampoo
some money
towel
blanket
bike
sandwich
swimming goggles
sweets
swimming costume
bag
water-wings
sack of potatoes

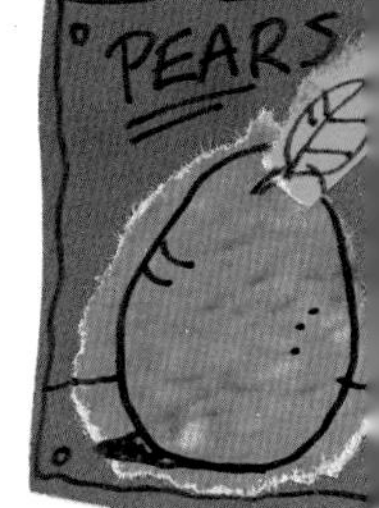

Going shopping

8 apples
15 satsumas
10 pears
8 bananas
2 oranges

Look at the lady's shopping list.

Which is the most popular fruit in her family?

____

How many fruits altogether is she going to have to carry home? ☐ fruits

Which fruits are equally popular with the family?

____

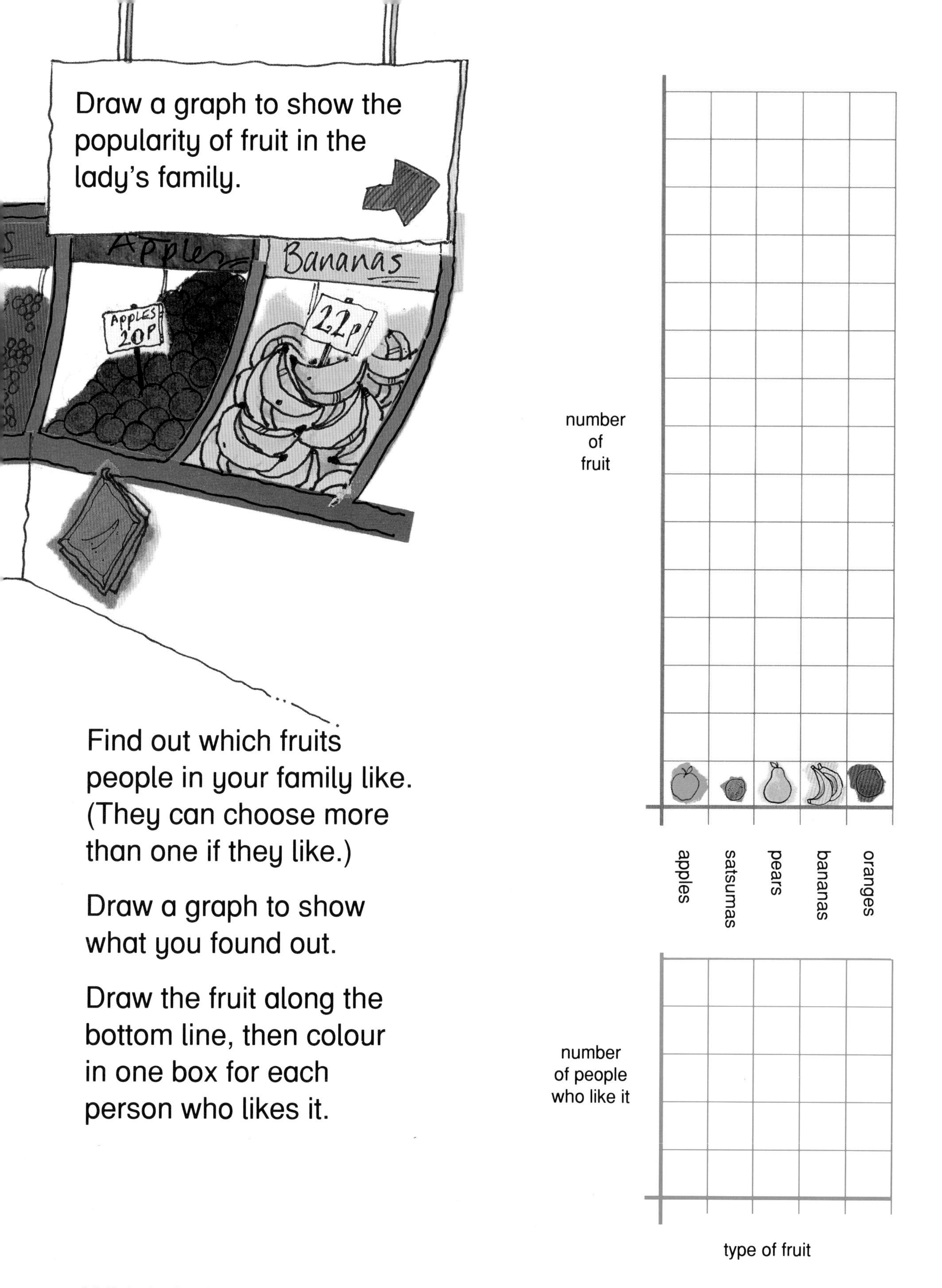

Draw a graph to show the popularity of fruit in the lady's family.

Find out which fruits people in your family like. (They can choose more than one if they like.)

Draw a graph to show what you found out.

Draw the fruit along the bottom line, then colour in one box for each person who likes it.

Which fruit is the most popular in your family?

Symmetry search

These patterns come from the tiles in the Alhambra Palace in Spain. They all have one or more lines of symmetry.

This pattern has one line of symmetry, because the middle strip is woven through the middle hexagon.

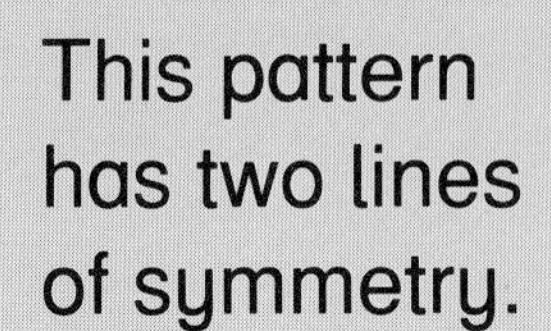

This pattern has two lines of symmetry.

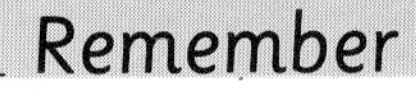

Remember

A line of symmetry has a perfect reflection on either side of it. You can check by putting the edge of a small mirror on the lines of symmetry that are drawn in. Is the reflection the same as the pattern in the book?

Can you draw one or more lines of symmetry on each of the patterns opposite?
Use a small mirror to help you. Answers on page 32.

Time off

This is the timetable of what the twins and their family did on their camping holiday.

Day	a.m.	p.m.
Monday	Arrive at Campsite	Boat trip round the harbour
Tuesday	All day on the beach	
Wednesday	Visit smuggling museum	Amusement park
Thursday	Swimming	Visit the lighthouse
Friday	All day walk to the castle and back	
Saturday	Shopping for souvenirs	Pack up and leave

Look at the timetable and answer these questions:

- How many days were the family on holiday? ____________
- When did they go to the museum? ____________
- On which days did they need a packed lunch? ____________
- Write down two more facts about the twins' holiday.

1 ____________

2 ____________

Supposing you could go anywhere and do anything you liked on holiday. Fill in your ideal holiday timetable.

Day	a.m.	p.m.
Monday		
Tuesday		
Wednesday		
Thursday		
Friday		
Saturday		

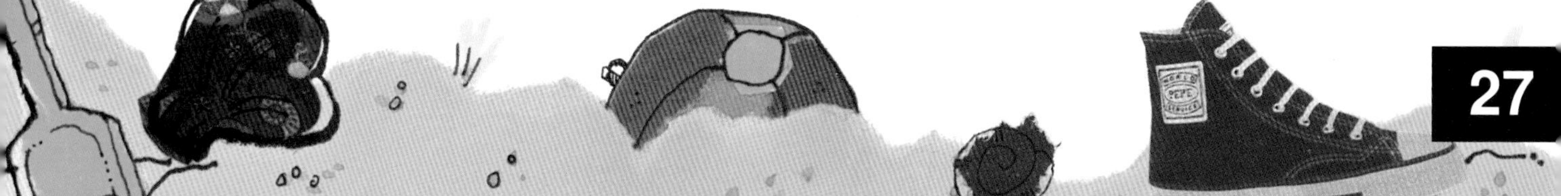

Family favourites

Carry out a survey of your family to find out each person's favourite colour, meal, sport, hobby and pop star.

name	favourite colour	favourite meal	favourite sport	favourit hobby

avourite pop star

Did you get the same answer from everyone for any question?

____

If yes, which one? ______________________________

Can you see any patterns for males and females (such as all the males liking the same colour or all the females liking the same sport)?

____

____

What else have you discovered from your survey?

____

____

Database

This computer shows how many boys and girls attend different clubs in their town.

HOBBY	BOYS	GIRLS	EVENING
youth club	152	135	Fri
judo	72	130	Wed
drama	40	35	Mon
dancing	10	52	Mon
chess	15	19	Fri
swimming	27	72	Thur

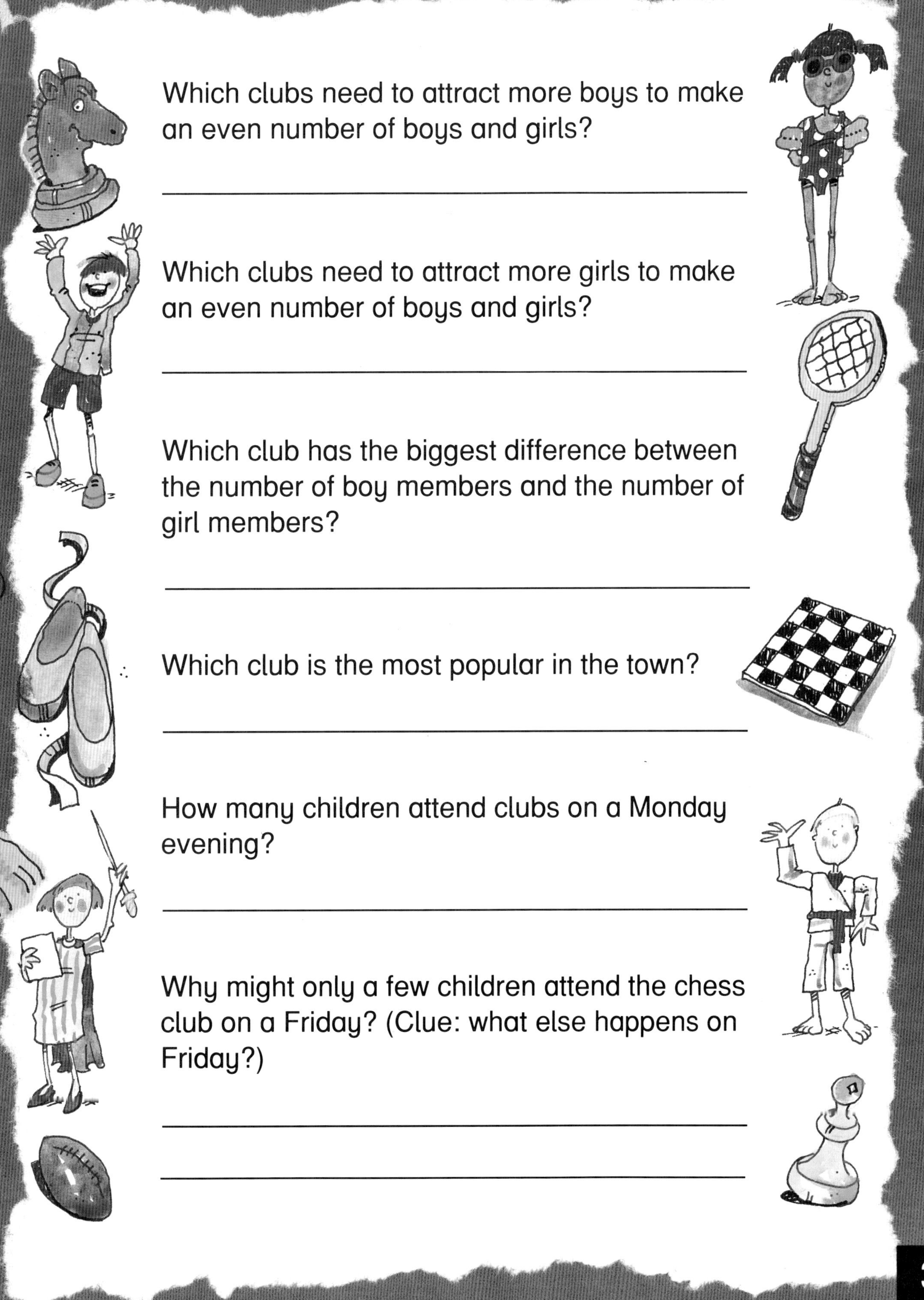

Which clubs need to attract more boys to make an even number of boys and girls?

____

Which clubs need to attract more girls to make an even number of boys and girls?

____

Which club has the biggest difference between the number of boy members and the number of girl members?

____

Which club is the most popular in the town?

____

How many children attend clubs on a Monday evening?

____

Why might only a few children attend the chess club on a Friday? (Clue: what else happens on Friday?)

____

____

MATHS SKILLS LINKS WITH THE NATIONAL CURRICULUM

ACTIVITY	USING AND APPLYING MATHEMATICS NAT 1	SHAPE AND SPACE NAT 4	HANDLING DATA NAT 5
Shape experiment	✓	✓	
Do you agree?			✓
Symmetry grids		✓	
Treasure hunt		✓	
Will it, won't it?			✓
Sort it out		✓	
Headstart quiz		✓	✓
Don't be a litterbug!	✓	✓	✓
Decisions, decisions			✓
Going shopping	✓		✓
Symmetry search		✓	
Time off			✓
Family favourites	✓		✓
Database			✓

ANSWERS

Pages 4–5 Shape experiment
1. The cylinder and sphere roll.
2. The cube, cuboid and cylinder stack.
3. The cube and cuboid have 6 faces.
4. The cylinder and sphere have 2 edges or less.

Pages 10–11 Treasure hunt
The treasure is in square numbers 2 and 29.

Pages 14–15 Sort it out
1. All the shapes have curves.
2. All the shapes have square corners.
3. All the shapes are symmetrical or regular.

Pages 16–17 Headstart quiz
1. Yes, octagons must have 8 sides.
2. SE (south-east).
3. A hexagon.
4. 18.
5. A rhinoceros.
6. 27.
7. No, it looks symmetrical, but no human being has identical sides of the body.
8. A cuboid.
9. 7.
10. A pentagon.

Pages 24–25

British Library Cataloguing in Publication Data
Clarke, Shirley
Headstart: Maths Skills: 7–9 — (Headstart)
I. Title II. Silsby, Barry
372.7

ISBN 0–340–57361–9

Typeset by Oxprint Limited, Oxford OX2 6TR
Printed in Great Britain for the educational publishing division of Hodder & Stoughton Ltd, Mill Road, Dunton Green, Sevenoaks, Kent by Cambus Litho, East Kilbride.

I LOVE SHELTIES

ANNUAL 2023

TECASSIA
PUBLISHING

Published in 2022 by

Tecassia Publishing
Building 31186
PO Box 6945
London
W1A 6US
www.tecassia.com

ISBN

Hardback 978-1-913916-14-5
Paperback 978-1-913916-15-2

Also available as an e-book 978-1-913916-13-8

Designed by Camilla Fellas Arnold

Dedication

🐾 🐾

Dedicated to Teddy, Anya, Blossom and Ziggie that were all featured in previous annual's but have since gone to rainbow bridge. Run free, dear shelties, until we meet again!

🐾 🐾

A portion of the proceeds of this book will be donated to
Pet Blood Bank UK
www.petbloodbankuk.org

Hello & Welcome

Welcome to the third edition of the *I Love Shelties Annual*. It's such an honour to bring this book to life every year and I love seeing how excited the sheltie community is to be part of it (and read it!)

From acorns, oak trees grow. What started as a pipe dream of an idea has already grown into a much anticipated project – we even had people get in touch to discuss what stories they want to send in for the 2024 edition. Each year the book gets bigger and bigger. This edition is double the size of the original annual!

I create this book as a passion project in my spare time, so this year in an effort to streamline the process, we experimented with an earlier submission period and a submission form to create more time for designing and an earlier publishing date, allowing people to buy copies for Christmas presents. This entire idea was born out of my own excitement at receiving *The Beano* and *Dandy* Christmas Annuals as a child, so to think that this is a gift someone will receive on Christmas Day fills me with so much joy.

To date we have raised £750 (approx $860). Our first edition raised £300 for The English Shetland Sheepdog Club's Welfare and Rescue Co-ordination. Last year's annual raised £450 which we have donated to *The Yorkshire Shetland Sheepdog Club's Rescue Co-ordination* efforts in the UK. This year we are donating proceeds from the sale of this book to *Pet Blood Bank UK*. I can't wait to see how much we can raise this year!

Finally I'd like to thank Gill King, Mark Witheridge and Vicky Harbour who sponsored the creation of this year's annual. Your sponsorship means so much and covers some of the costs of the book production meaning we can donate more money to charity from the book sales!

Camilla

Camilla Fellas Arnold
Editor in Chief

CONTENTS

MEET OUR COVER STAR!

This year was such a tough decision to choose a cover that we put it up for a public vote. We had over 1,300 votes on our Facebook page (www.facebook.com/ iloveshelties worldwide) so we wanted to introduce you to our wonderful cover star and two gorgeous runners up!

Words and photos from Melinda Kosik

Lucky-Luke Star Nature Dark Eastern was born on 15th May 2021 at Lucky-Luke kennel in Hungary. I had to wait eight months for him but it was absolutely worth it. I decided a couple of years ago that I would like to have a sheltie. I searched and read a lot about the breed and contacted several breeders. My original plan was to have a sheltie female and name her Leila. However, Tímea Kaka, the breeder I was in contact with, suggested having a sheltie male for the first time so I got Lucius.

He is my first dog. The first two months were hard but we've learned a lot from each other and he became the best dog for us. Lucius has learned so fast and we practice a lot every day. We spend a lot of time together as I work from home. He has a really curious personality, everything is interesting for him.

We love to explore new places, learn new tricks, play with friends, play with a ball, long walks and watch sunsets. We are going to try herding this autumn.

I started to learn photography in May and Lucius is a fantastic model, he always inspires me. During Pixelkontent's photography course we asked him to sit on the elegant armchair and he was sitting as if he was on a throne like a king!

Above the city on Budaörs Kő-hegy (Stone hill). Facing page: Taken on the Pixelkontent photography course

Every day is a gift with him; he is special, calm, funny, smart and always curious. We are so grateful to have him in our family: Márk, Melinda and Lucius.

COVER STAR RUNNER UP

Shanel is one and lives in France. Her owner Coline had always dreamt of having a Shetland Sheepdog so Shanel is a dream come true. She's happy, sporty, cheerful and affectionate but does like to run after sheep!

Words and photos by Coline Van Amerongen

Reglisse des Gardiens du Flot Bleu, 2 years old, Bicolour black Shetland Sheepdog, living happily in France.

COVER STAR RUNNER UP

Reglisse is two and lives in France with his older brother Pixel (three years old). He loves his brother and will not hesitate to protect him, he's very kind. Reglisse is a very active dog, one of his passions is frisbee catching. He can jump high but always lands back on his feet.

Words and photos by Luc Stepniewski

SUPPORTING PET BLOOD BANK UK

We are donating proceeds from this year's annual to Pet Blood Bank UK. We spoke to them and they shared some information about what they do and how the money we raise will help them.

What is Pet Blood Bank?

Pet Blood Bank is a charity set up to support vets by providing a blood service for pets, just like the one we have as humans. The charity runs donation sessions across the country, where owners bring their beloved companions to give blood. Pet Blood Bank operates 24 hours a day, seven days a week, to ensure blood is always available for pets in need.

Every unit of donated blood can help to save the lives of up to four other dogs.

What dogs can donate blood?

Pet Blood Bank is looking for owners of large, happy, healthy, and confident dogs to become blood donors. Shelties, lovely as they are, are unfortunately too small a breed of dog to be able to donate (but we'll tell you how you can help!).

To become a blood donor, dogs must be:

- Fit and healthy
- Between one and eight years old
- Weigh more than 25kg
- Confident and enjoy meeting new people

Do dogs have different blood types?

Yes! Just like humans, dogs have different blood types. They can either be DEA 1 positive or negative. Negative blood is in high demand as this can be given to a dog in an emergency, so there is a need for more dogs who are likely to have this blood type to come forward as donors. For this reason, Pet Blood Bank is particularly appealing to you to ask owners of the following breeds to consider registering their dogs. We're sure there are many Shelties who are friends with these other breeds:

- Airedale Terrier
- American Bulldog
- Basset Hound
- Bearded Collie
- Border Collie
- Boxer
- Curly Coated Retriever
- Dobermann
- Dogue de Bordeaux
- English Bull Terrier
- Flat Coated Retriever
- German Shepherd
- Greyhound
- Lurcher
- Saluki
- Old English Sheepdog
- Weimaraner

How you can get involved?

Even though Shelties are too small a breed to be able to donate blood themselves, there are still other ways you can help the charity such as donating proceeds from the sales of this book!. Owners can also get involved and help Pet Blood Bank through fundraising, volunteering, and raising awareness.

Fundraising

By fundraising for Pet Blood Bank, you will help to save the lives of pets across the country. Every effort, big or small, counts.

Any money you raise will allow Pet Blood Bank to provide more blood to dogs in need, as well as invest for the future through research and education.

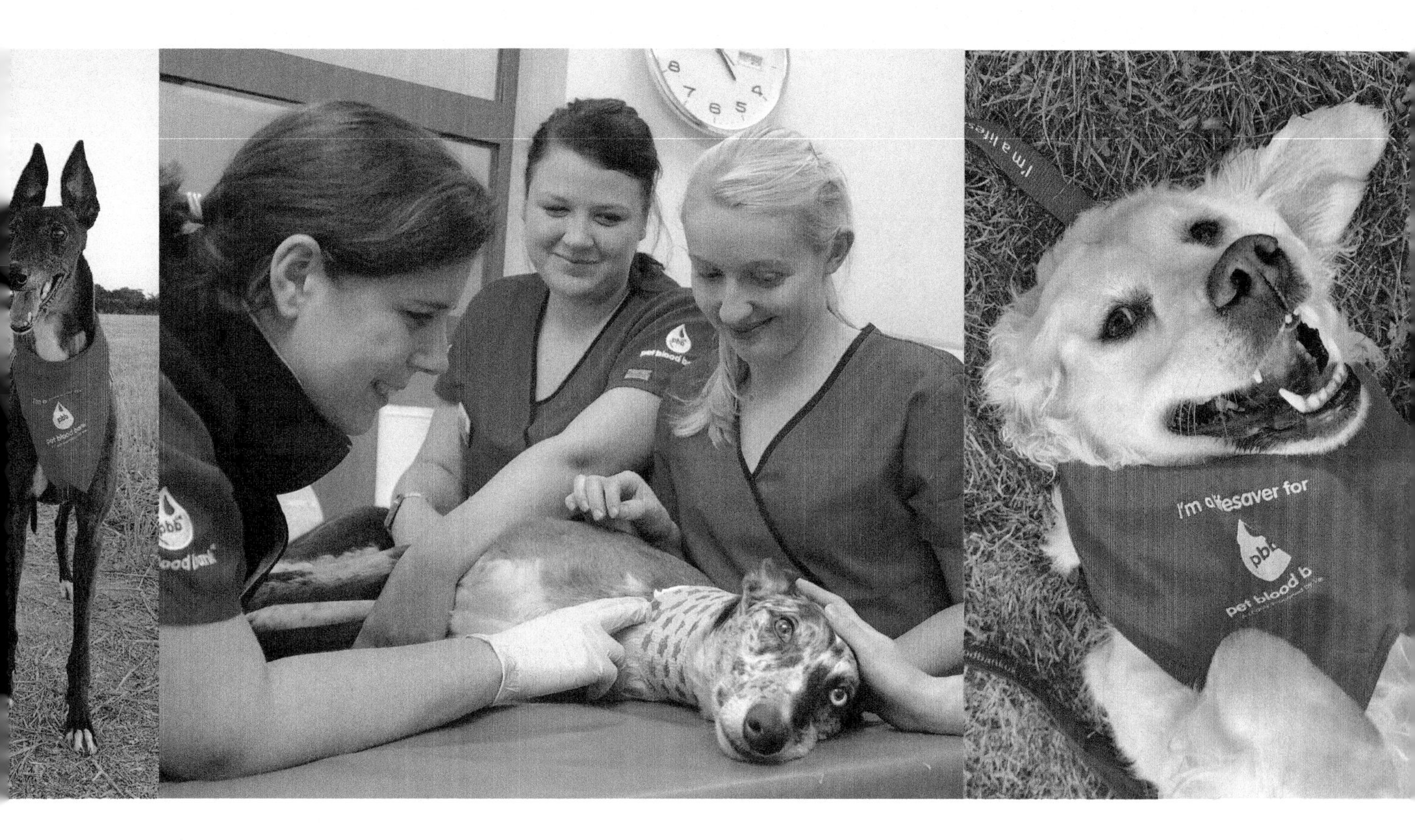

From taking on a sponsored run or challenge to hosting your own event, there are plenty of ways you can get involved and fundraise for Pet Blood Bank. Get creative, have fun, and know that the funds you raise will make a big difference to the lives of pets.

Volunteering

Volunteers play a vital role in helping to save the lives of pets. There are a range of opportunities so we hope you will find something that inspires you.

- You can help at donation sessions – Donation sessions are busy days and an extra pair of hands can always make a huge difference. You can help ensure the session is a great experience for all donor dogs and their owners. This involves helping to set up for the session, meeting and greeting the lovely lifesavers, and taking their photos for Pet Blood Bank's Facebook page. The best part, though, is giving out plenty of hugs and treats to the donors and having a friendly chat with their owners, exchanging fun stories about each other's wonderful dog.
- Join Pet Blood Bank at the events – we are very lucky to be asked to attend lots of local events, such as dog shows and fairs. These events usually take place at weekends and could be anything from a few hours to a full day. The charity will provide you with everything you need for the stall and give you some training on attending events, so you just need to go along and spread the good word.

Spreading the word

Lastly, another easy way to get involved is to simply help spread the word among your friends, family, and community. There is always a big need for more owners to bring their pets to donate. If you know anyone with a pet that might make a good donor, please let them know about Pet Blood Bank. You can also email *supporter@petbloodbankuk.org* to request some leaflets to give out to your friends and community.

Learn more

To find out more about Pet Blood Bank or to get involved in the charity, please visit www.petbloodbankuk.org

Third Time Lucky!

We are so lucky to have so many loyal fans of this annual and we really couldn't do it without you – here's to you, we hope you enjoy the third I Love Shelties Annual!

At one point I wasn't sure if it would be possible to create an annual this year and was looking at the very real prospect of having to cancel the third edition.

In order to give people more time to get hold of copies of the book (distribution of the hardback version on Amazon has been an ongoing challenge for the past two years), I decided to have a longer submissions window earlier in the year. I hoped it would give me ample time to get the annual ready and put through the relevant channels so that hardback copies would be readily available.

However this longer submissions window meant that submissions were thin on the ground for quite some time. The deadline was extended and fortunately we had a flurry of submissions in the last two weeks that meant the third edition was a go! A special thank you goes to my mum Jeanette Fellas who always does a stellar job of reminding and mobilising people every year.

I want to say a great big THANK YOU to everyone that takes the time to write stories, send in photos and buy copies of the annual so we can donate to charity. It is a joy to create and I love seeing the photos you send of your shelties enjoying the annual every year.

My wish is that the annual grows in popularity and reach year on year so we can raise as much money as possible for good causes. This year I have chosen Pet Blood Bank UK as our charity that we'll be donating proceeds towards.

Blood can be vital for animals in surgery so it's hugely important work that this charity does. Dogs must weigh over 25kg in order to be able to donate blood which obviously a sheltie would never be able to do, so I thought we could do the next best thing and support their cause by raising money for them to continue to do their incredible work. We'll be announcing how much we've raised for them in next year's annual!

Above: Badger

Facing page clockwise from top right: Breccan, Keeko, Chip, Roxy, Joy and Wee Charlie

HARLIE
CES BACK
LEGION OF FANS
HERE COMES TROUBLE!
SENIOR SHELTIES
GUISE
Bentley says 'Yee Haw! I'm a Cowboy!' Make sure you watch out for Sheriff Leone though!
Roxy
Pepper
Aline getting into the Easter spirit
Toby, waiting with his kitty pal for trick or treaters
I LOVE SHELTIES ANNUAL 2022

HALL OF FAME

We receive so many photos and stories in the making of this book from shelties all around the world. We wanted to include as many beautiful faces as possible so welcome to our sheltie 'hall of fame'!

Laci from Syracuse, New York

The Mosardi gang from Hertfordshire, UK

Pepsi, 10 from Shetland, UK

Little Twist at 6 weeks old from East Sussex, UK

Shadow 8.5, and Onyx 6 from Brisbane, Australia

Duskie (left), 9 and Tess (right), 6 from Cumbria, UK

Bonnie, 2 from Perth, UK

Roxy with her mum and siblings from Hampshire, UK

Pippin from Illinois, USA

Aline from Budapest, Hungary

Badger, 1 from Cambridgeshire UK

Keeko, 7 from Arbroath , UK

Piper from Bedlington UK

Our favourite Sheltie mix Laddie from Greenwood, Arkansas, USA

Dusty from Arkansas, USA

Frosty from Illinois, USA

Sir Tavish, 4 from New South Wales, Australia

Bernie and Rolo from Devon, UK

Tansy and Lady from Peterborough, UK

Levi from Arkansas, USA

Teddy-Boo, 3 from Norfolk, UK

Daisy, 11 and Zorro, 4 from Bath, UK

Roxy from Illinois, USA

Lucy, 10 from North Carolina, USA

Gracie, Glory, Enya and Blossom from Lincolnshire, UK

Aja, Raya, Faith, Falcon, Ella from Florida, USA

Freya, 2 from Kent, UK

Chip from Fort Worth, Texas, USA

Cooper from Illinois, USA

Maya, 20 months (left) and Luna, 4 from Carmarthen, UK

Miss Tallahassee from Dorset, UK

Lassie, 4, Ben, 12 and puppy Tango from Aberdeenshire, Scotland, UK

Biscuit and Cricket from Ontario, Canada

Harry from the UK

Copper from Illinois, USA

Bryn, Charli and Jordie from New Zealand

Laddie, 9 from Hull, UK

Wee Charlie, 10 with his mum Beauly, 13 and niece DaisyMay, 6 from Aberdeenshire Scotland

Mum Gia and her son Biscuit from Winnipeg, Manitoba Canada

Rosie, 3 from the UK

Picardy, 14 from Centerville, Ohio, USA

Echo from Centerville, Ohio, USA

Finn, 4 and Laddie, 1 from Dunedin, New Zealand

Fizz and her son Chip, from East Sussex, UK

Encore from Centerville, Ohio, USA

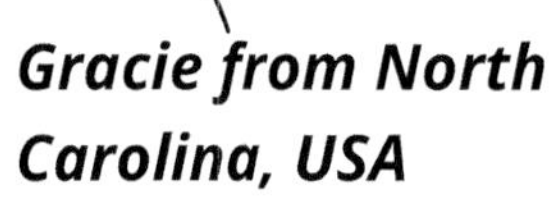

Gracie from North Carolina, USA

Maggie Mae (right) and Finnegan (left) from New York, USA

L to R: Mia, Teddy and Talia from Norfolk, UK

Wavesong Chasing Rainbows, 10 months from East Sussex, UK. Photo by Julia Carr.

Teddy (left) and Ollie (right) from Helsby, UK

River from Illinois, USA

Maysie May, Jazz, Halo and Millie from Brackley, UK

L to R: Rosie, Poppy, Libby, Sadie & Anya from Carmarthen, UK

Breccan, 5 from Ohio, USA

L to R: Ben, Bramble and Rosie from Norfolk, Uk

Shanel, 1 from Le Thor, France

Cali, 4 from Berkshire, UK

Dory, 4 from Hampshire, UK

Left back:Tai, right back: Darcey, left front: Ziggi, right front: Indy. Owned by Tracey and Bernadette Baudains. Photography by P.C. Photography.

Authors:
Nadiya Goga, sheltie owner, Bratislava, Slovakia
Diana, VIPSHELTIE kennel (FCI), Kyiv, Ukraine
Elena Plakuschaia, sheltie owner, Kyiv, Ukraine
Veronika Kovalenko, sheltie owner, Kyiv region, Ukraine
Inna Kalnibolotskaya, CHARIVNE NAMYSTO kennel (FCI), Kyiv region, Ukraine
Larisa Rozhkova, Elven Garden kennel (FCI), Kyiv, Ukraine
Elizaveta Nemno, IZ PITERSKIKH VOLKOV kennel, Zaporizhzhia region, Ukraine

Translators UA-ENG:
Liliana Tarapatska, Lviv, Ukraine
Nadiya Goga, Bratsilava, Slovakia

ESCAPING UKRAINE

"And now, when you are reading this article, I don't know, if we are still alive or not.

Ukraine is a European country that was attacked by its neighbour. Russian bombs aimed at not only military targets but also civilian ones like maternity hospitals, schools, kindergartens, universities and the entire infrastructure of the country. Civilians, women, children, men, old people are dying... Russia hates Ukraine for its independence, for its freedom and for the fact that Ukraine does not want to be part of Russia. But real war brings death and suffering not only to people but to animals as well.

There are 18 Ukrainian sheltie kennels registered in FCI (Fédération Cynologique Internationale). All of them felt in their own skin what war in the 21st century means. Some of them had to flee from Donetsk and Luhansk in 2014 previously and now are forced to save themselves again. Some of them can't leave their houses and have to stay in danger either under bombing or in occupied territory without access to food and water. Some of them managed to escape and now live the hard life of refugees abroad.

A few of these kennels and sheltie owners agreed to tell their stories. Some of them had to overcome many losses and difficulties, some might seemingly have had easier escapes and don't have to hear the sound of rockets every day. All of them nevertheless know very well what it is to fear for the life of their relatives and their pets and what it's like to be not sure if you will survive the next few hours or not.

Diana, VIPSHELTIE kennel (FCI), Kyiv, Ukraine

We are a small sheltie kennel from Kyiv. We have four fluffy family members: Anfiska, 9, Barney, 6, Chelsea and Candy, both 2, while the fifth family member, Tiffany, 11, lives abroad at that moment. Our story is maybe not as tragic as others, but I do believe that every story matters and stories like ours have to exist to give hope in happy endings.

February 24th, 5:00 AM - our peaceful life ended. We entered into another reality and its name is "WAR". Massive explosions woke us up and the glass in windows was rattling. At first, we did not understand what had happened, our consciousness still tried to break through the remains of a dream. Disbelief was our first thought: "There should be a normal explanation, it is probably an incident somewhere".

However ten minutes later we heard another powerful explosion and everything became clear – what we were afraid to say aloud, Russian troops began shelling Kyiv. The dogs were afraid; they jumped on the bed and barked loudly. Anfisa started howling. There was no telecom signal which frightened us even more. Lack of knowledge tore apart our minds.

Fortunately, the Internet worked but nothing was on the news. Only through Facebook from our friends did we find out that not only Kyiv but also other large cities of Ukraine were being bombed. I wish you could understand what was going on in my mind at that moment.

Stupid thoughts like whether public transport was still working and that I probably should call work to tell them that it looks like I won't come today, mixed with questions like can I go to walk my dogs, aren't they afraid of the explosions, do I have enough food and how long we can survive in occupation or should we escape?

I was afraid to stay at home, as a rocket had already hit one of the houses in the city. I was

L to R: Tiffany, Anfisa, Candy, Barney and Chelsea

Barney and Anfisa, facing page: Tiffany

after the very first rocket explosions and it appeared to be a very wise decision.

Luckily bridges were not hit but were blocked to slow down the advance of enemy troops in case they invaded the city. Had my daughter and her boyfriend stayed at home a bit longer, they wouldn't have been able to come and rescue us from this hell.

We packed the car with everything necessary for dogs like food, leashes, medications and ointments in case of any emergency during the trip, carry bags, toys, disposable and reusable diapers. An ordinary person might think that our small car was a pet shop on wheels.

afraid to go out. Nobody knew what was going on outside. It took a few seconds for me to realise that we didn't have any other choice but to save our dogs. We could have imagined living in an occupied city ourselves, but the image of being not able to walk, feed or heal them in case of need was unbearable.

The only driver in our family is my younger daughter's boyfriend. They live on the left bank of the river Dnipro, which crosses the city of Kyiv while I live on the right bank. My mother, who went through WW2 shared her experience a lot with us. She told us how she had to cross the bridge when German soldiers entered her town. Bridges are one of the first targets and that particular bridge was blown up right behind her after she managed to cross the river.

People who didn't make it were captured by Germans and taken to working camps. Remembering this story, just a few days before the 24th of February, my older daughter forced us to agree that if Russia attacked, my younger daughter with her boyfriend would drive to me. They headed out immediately

Personal belongings? We took only a laptop and some snacks to refresh ourselves on the way. We filled the car with a full tank and started our unplanned journey. We chose Slovakia, as my older daughter has been living there for some time already. It also helped us to accept the idea of escape, we weren't fleeing, we were going to visit her.

We travel a lot with our shelties, they are used to it and enjoy looking out of the window, watching the scenery passing by, barking at dogs and people outside, what could be better? This time though, they understood that something wrong was happening and sat calmly in their places, looking at us questioningly with their almond shaped eyes.

Our optimistic estimations to reach Lviv by late evening were crushed by cruel reality. All three lanes of the highway were filled with cars. Young people, probably students whose classes were cancelled, were walking along the side of the road with backpacks. Apparently they were returning home from Kyiv to their parents.

During the whole day, we drove only 30km because the entire row of cars on the highway was simply standing without any movement. We didn't have enough food with us but the greatest risk was being hit by a Russian rocket. Shelling continued. A long row of cars in an open area was a perfect target. At one point we even got a crazy thought to turn back home.

We wanted to be back in our cosy flat, comfortable beds and hot supper. However, news that Russian forces were shelling Chernobyl station spurred us on. We still remember the consequences of its explosion in 1986. Were something to happen in Chernobyl, we wanted to be as far away as possible from there, so we had no other choice anymore. We could no longer drive forward or backwards and had to spend the night right in the car on the side of the road.

The next day we managed to get to Zhytomyr only. The road which usually takes two hours took us the whole day. The city still waking up to the new morning, met us with sounds of sirens for air alarm. Russian missiles were bombing Zhytomyr airport which is only 5km far from the city and even a small mistake in ballistic calculations could have led to a massive hit on the city itself.

Instead of tasty croissants and hot coffee for breakfast – two hours in a cold shelter without a signal, not being able to inform our friends that we were okay and not able to get any news. But we didn't complain at all, we are thankful to the people who let us in with four dogs.

Not all people in shelters were so generous. We know stories when people with pets were not let inside shelters and were forced to stay outside as they understandably didn't want to leave their pets. When it was all clear, the highway was still filled with cars and we decided to spend some time in a small village nearby.

Away from the highway, far from big cities, it was so peaceful there. Welcoming hosts, delicious homemade food and our shelties rejoicing in the opportunity to spend time outside. All that happened the day before seemed to be just a bad dream. For a moment we wanted to stay there for a few more days, till Ukrainian forces expelled Russian invaders from our land. We couldn't accept that it might last for months, who knows, maybe even years. But reality was cruel in its honesty.

Shelling continued, Russian troops were coming closer and closer, some bridges were already blown up and there was not much fuel left at tank stations. A few more days in this illusion of peace and calmness could make it impossible to escape. We wished good luck to our hosts and drove to Lviv.

Another frightening surprise awaited us on our way. Something happened to the car, oil was leaking from the engine. All car service stations on our way were closed, as people were afraid to go outside their houses without necessity. The probability of stopping in the middle of the village road was extremely high. We were desperate.

I believe that our shelties are our angels, they not only support us in hard moments of our life just being themselves and being around, but they also bring us luck. I strongly believe that it was a miracle that we managed to get to Lviv and found an open service station there.

Thanks to good people, we also got a roof over our heads. There we met two of our friends who also by their own means made their way from Kyiv to Lviv. One woman with a three year old child and a cat and another woman with two dogs, a Chinese Crested and Papillion.

When the car was fixed, we continued the journey together: a small car with five adults, six dogs, a child and a cat in it. It is unbelievable how an 800km long distance can turn into almost a week's journey.

Yet more bad luck was to befall us when our driver had to stay in Ukraine. There was already martial law in force and he was not allowed to leave the country. My daughter decided to stay with him. Oh, I wished I could go back with them, my heart was tearing apart. But this would mean that all suffering we'd been through, all uncertainty about our future, and all our anxiety and fear along the way were for nothing. *You should think about the shelties,* my daughter told me. With a heart full of pain I went in the direction of the state border, thinking about if I would ever see them again.

At the moment when I'm writing this text they are still in Kyiv and every day I pray for them that they are safe. It is more than four months since we got to Slovakia. We experienced a very chaotic March and April when we helped our friends to escape from Ukraine to Europe and even to the USA.

Even though I have already evacuated to another country I still have a fear of loud noises. I still feel ringing in the ears of the air sirens and still feel uncomfortable when I hear loud sounds or see a helicopter in the sky.

When thunder rumbles, I fear that this is the sound of a missile explosion and that war caught me even here. We feel guilty for our friends and fellow countrymen who are not able to flee and do our best to help other refugees and those who stayed in Ukraine.

I should also add that we for sure wouldn't manage it psychically without our fluffy family members. They got used to a new place of living very fast and support us in sharing their joy and love for life with everybody. And I want to say it again – shelties fluffy angels that

Elena Plakuschaia with her shelties above and right

took care of us on the earth. I strongly believe that it won't be a long time before we can go back home, hug our loved ones, walk and play in the forest near our house again.

Elena Plakuschaia, sheltie owner, Kyiv, Ukraine

I'm from Kyiv and the owner of two marvellous shelties, a mother from the Iz Piterskich Volkov kennel and her daughter. It was not an accident how I got my first sheltie. I've been doing agility with German Shepherds since 2014.

When my Shepherd got old, I looked for a future champion and chose a sheltie puppy - Karen Iz Piterskich Volkov, pet name Kara. She came into my life in 2017. Since then we did a lot together: agility, herd sheep and dog-pulling. In 2021, Kara had four admirable puppies. There was one lovely sable girl among them and I decided to keep her for myself to continue an active life: agility, herding and other dog sports.

But sadly on 24th February, everything changed dramatically. The war came so very close to Kyiv. The thought of evacuation was out of the question. I am a doctor and our institution continued to work, which means that I also had to work.

But those days, instead of the usual active walks, agility training and trips to herd sheep, walks were limited to patrolling the city streets among barricades and checkpoints, often accompanied by the sound of heart-rending air sirens. Several times we had to hurry to hide in a bomb shelter. Believe me, you don't want to experience such a walk, it doesn't bring you any pleasure.

Luckily, my shelties did not react to air alarms and sounds of distant explosions. They rather didn't understand why our walks are so strange, no balls, pullers, agility, or beloved sheep. When the curfew lasted 36 hours and we had to quickly run out and come back home, they probably just read my thoughts, quickly, quickly.

Hard conditions of daily dog owner life lasted for two months. A man can get used to everything, but why should we do this? We had so many plans for the future but our whole world collapsed in a second! Nevertheless, I believe that everything will be okay! One day Ukraine will win and we will get back to our training, to our sheep and our friends!

Veronika Kovalenko, sheltie owner, Kyiv region, Ukraine

Before the war, my family and I lived in a village near Makariv in the Buchanskyi district. My husband and I, our four kids (the youngest was just four months old) and our disabled grandma used to have a happy life. We have a Shetland sheepdog Adel from Iz Nochikh Volkov (ACW) / Iz Piterskikh Volkov (FCI) kennel and a cat.

Our pets were free, they spent lots of time outside chasing the wind in our yard and in the fields nearby. During the first days of this horrible war, we hoped that it was going to end very soon, we had this illusion that everything would be the way it used to be. But at the end of that awful February, the electricity got cut off for months. For us, it meant that the heating and water supply was also cut off because everything is dependent on electricity. We could not cook food and it was cold.

We could hear aviation just above our house, we were not able to walk the dog, because it was extremely dangerous, she was scared and even didn't want to go outside. The air siren was so frequent that we were practically forced to sleep in our basement.

At first, we took Adel with us to the basement, but it is so small and dark that she was too scared to stay there. So we decided to leave her upstairs with our grandma. This continued for five days but the kids got sick. They started coughing because of the high humidity, not to mention they were really scared.

Veronika Kovalenko's dauther and sheltie Adel

The village was sieged. Russian occupying forces entrenched themselves in the villages nearby, that's why our home village got cut off from the highway. People were trying to escape in their cars, even though there were no green corridors. Every day the war was closer.

We learned how to distinguish the sound of rockets, shelling, bombing and air defence. It was a relief to hear our air defence, it meant that our troops were defending us. But in general, the situation was extremely difficult, not everybody was lucky enough to escape. We often received news about Russian forces firing on civilian vehicles, it was hell on earth.

I would also like to mention the group of dog owners from our district whom we trust. We had a chat where we shared information about the situation in our villages, about the numbers and location of enemy vehicles and military.

This message then was delivered to our forces and within a couple of minutes, the enemies were destroyed. We also advised on how to support each other and how to help our pets.

One day our neighbours managed to find a way through the fields to escape and get to our forces. They secretly shared the details about this way and we decided to try and give it a try. We took only two backpacks for seven people, just in case we would be running on foot.

We had no idea how our plan would work out because of the kids, grandma and our dog. We were preparing for different situations, even the worst-case scenario.

So we packed the essentials and hit the road no matter what was awaiting ahead. The road was difficult and dangerous, we drove through the fields, found a highway, passed through the remains of destroyed civilian cars and military vehicles and tanks and finally reached the checkpoint. Ukrainian checkpoint! It was a relief! We drove to the western part of Ukraine and then to Germany where our relatives were already waiting for us.

We drove for 72 hours. We spent 16 hours on the border before we reached another universe it seemed. A universe where we did not have to worry for our lives, where we did not see the savage invaders or enemy aviation, where there were no air sirens, and where people were smiling and living happily.

Meanwhile, our village was occupied. Our friends were killed in the woods or simply vanished never to be found. Now Kyiv is freed from Russian soldiers, there is no active combat there, but every day Russians try to shell and bomb our capital city as well as all the other parts of Ukraine.

The Charivne Namysto Kennel Family

However, the demining work is already in full swing: sappers are working on land and in water for the safety of their fellow citizens. They are carrying out demining in the Kyiv region. But despite the hard work it is not one hundred percent safe to walk in the parks, fields or beaches yet.

As for our beloved Adel, she was so brave on the road and now she is learning to live in this new world. She's coping with everything perfectly, because for dogs and their owners, humans are everything they need for real happiness.

Inna Kalnibolotskaya, CHARIVNE NAMYSTO kennel (FCI), Kyiv region, Ukraine

Shetland sheepdog kennel CHARIVNE NAMYSTO aka SheltiePark is located in Selychivka village in the Kyiv region not far from Boryspil International Airport. Apart from the kennel, there is a small shelter for dogs and cats and a pet hotel. Besides this, we have some other animals, namely goats, hedgehogs and chickens.

As of the 24th of February, when the full-fledged war started, 58 dogs and cats lived in our home. It was an enormous responsibility. We had little information about what exactly was going on, we had no idea what to do in the first place. Fortunately, we always have some food supply for us and our animals.

Understandably, with that many animals, it is complicated to have enough food for longer periods. From the first day of the war, we tried to make our house safer. We blocked our windows with plastic foam and chipboard, which reduced the sounds of explosions. A lot of the animals are afraid of loud noises and we tried to make them as comfortable as possible.

We have a large house and a basement, so we decided to move underground with all of the

The Charivne Namysto Kennel Family in happier times

animals. We took all the kennels and crates, medicines, warm blankets, water, and food for us and our pets. My son with his family and his pets also came to our place.

Only later on did we find out that the Russian military was very close. Many villages nearby were occupied by Russians. We could hear explosions, shelling and bombing. Since there are many rivers in the vicinity, the bridges were blown up to slow down the Russian invasion and this is what helped us to stay alive.

All shops and drug stores were closed. Some of our animals needed veterinary help but they were closed too. We were running out of food.

From the first day of the war, we kept in touch with other sheltie owners. We created a Viber group and tried to encourage each other in this difficult situation. All the neighbours were really understanding and friendly, we tried to share everything we could.

A bit later we were able to evacuate some of the animals from our pet hotel. Sadly, not everyone survived the road. After some time, we managed to evacuate the animals whose owners were in other counties.

For a long time, we were not able to get pet food, but during the evacuation of civilians from the pet hotel, volunteers brought us food and petrol. This helped us a lot. We shared everything with other kennels.

Since our kennel has lots of friends and tries to keep in touch with the owners of our shelties, together with a Doberman help team in Ukraine we were able to organise food deliveries to Kyiv. One Doberman was left in our pet hotel, and later the dog was evacuated abroad and found his new family there.

Constant care for our animals helped us go on. When Ukrainian Armed Forces freed the neighbouring villages from Russian occupants, we took in a dog with a broken paw and before that, we had also taken in a sheltie with a fracture. We were exhausted. We were worried about our dogs in Kharkiv, Zhytomyr and Kyiv regions which were under heavy attacks.

We are extremely happy that our friends were finally able to evacuate. Unfortunately, not all of them have a place to come back to, since Russian invaders destroyed numerous buildings. Our friends from Lviv supported us and even devised an evacuation plan. But we made up our minds and stayed at home.

The neighbouring villages suffered a lot. People were killed, animals were slaughtered and houses were ruined. Some of the owners of our dogs live in the occupied territory in the Kherson region. They cannot evacuate and we are extremely worried about them.

Like many people in Ukraine, we practically lost our jobs overnight. Of course, we still have some savings. We get some help from our friends from abroad, we received humanitarian help and it gives us the possibility to survive. We hope for their help in future.

For now, there are 21 Sheltie dogs, four Doberman dogs, nine cats, ten mix breed dogs, four goats, five hedgehogs and chickens. Some of the animals will be delivered to their owners abroad eventually.

I would like to mention my handler friend Ania and her family. They live in Mykulychi near Borodianka. From the first day of the war, they gave shelter to a mother with her child and dogs. They were staying in a small basement under constant shooting and shelling. It was a sheer miracle that they were able to evacuate to the Khmelnytskyi region.

The Charivne Namysto family receiving dog food as humanitarian aid

But because of the war, they were left with nothing to live on. Later on, we managed to send them some dog food and they received humanitarian help. Now they have come back home and fortunately, their home was not ruined. We still keep in touch and we are happy that they are safe.

We believe in miracles and justice. Our animals deserve a happy and peaceful life, they don't deserve this brutal war, which is a real crime against humanity. There is no forgiveness for us to the killers.

Larisa Rozhkova, Elven Garden kennel (FCI), Kyiv, Ukraine

We are a small Shetland Sheepdog kennel from Ukraine. Currently, we have five dogs: Luna, Diva, Finick whom we bought just three months before the Russian war in Ukraine and our older dogs Messi and Zizu. There was a time when we used to attend dog shows and were dreaming of breeding. But our plans and dreams got shattered with the full-fledged invasion of Russia into Ukraine.

We live in the capital city of Kyiv. Therefore when the Russian military started shelling and bombing Kyiv, we decided to move to our house in the country. We thought that together with our dogs we would be safer there. We also gave shelter to some of our friends with their dogs.

Unfortunately, our house appeared to be in the centre of combat, the territory was the target of devastating weapon strikes and we were subjected to heavy bombing. This period was marked by the massive use of explosive weapons in populated areas. We were scared.

The Elven Garden Kennel

Constant explosions. Constant fear for our lives. Our dogs were trembling with every loud sound, they were frightened. We lived in this madness for three weeks. We had nowhere to run, nowhere to flee, nowhere to hide. We don't have any shelter for such emergencies.

The battlefield became closer and closer with each day. We couldn't go back because the bridges had been destroyed. So we had only one choice – to run to the western part of Ukraine.

We took our dogs and left everything else behind, we didn't take any clothes, any possessions. We understood that it was extremely dangerous, but we braced ourselves and we ran.

We got lucky – we found a cheap house to live in and people accommodated us with our five dogs and a cat. The conditions were not too good, the house was really small, and there was no water or other facilities in the building, but we were safe. The explosions and shooting were far from us so despite all the air alarms we could breathe.

We lived there for 50 days. It was absolutely unbearable, psychologically. The time was passing and spring blooming. We were longing to go back home. I dreamt about coming back to my garden.

So it was decided that we were heading back home! Now we are taking one day at a time, we are living by the day. We believe in our glorious victory over the enemy! I hope my magical elven garden will save us!

Elizaveta Nemno, IZ PITERSKIKH VOLKOV kennel, Zaporizhzhia region, Ukraine

We are the owners of the IZ PITERSKIKH VOLKOV kennel, which is located in Zaporizhzhia, Ukraine. We live outside the city in the direction of Donetsk. Our story is not so colourful, as we didn't flee.

Before the war, we lived a calm family life, made a lot of plans for our future and the future of our kennel, and planned a lot of things to do to develop it. It was a calm life, we loved to walk along the river with our shelties. But one day it all collapsed.

Nowadays Russian artillery is shelling villages, killing peaceful people just 20km from our house. Sometimes their rockets fall just a few kilometres from us. We may not leave our

Iz Piterskikh Volkov Shelties

kennel because in case of heavy bombing we have to take care that all animals go downstairs to the basement to stay safe.

All our walks are possible now only on the territory of the kennel and only at certain times, between air alarms. Food portions are reduced, but we try to do our best for our animals.

Unfortunately, we are forced to violate the curfew and have to work and walk the dogs at night in complete darkness without light. Nevertheless, we decided to stay and help people, their pets and domestic animals in the occupied territories.

We are trying to find humanitarian aid, and send food and medicine to people and animals that are under occupation. Unfortunately, we spend a lot of money on it, as postage prices are high and people who agree to take packages to occupied territories ask a lot for it as it is extremely dangerous. They risk their lives.

However, we try to help people and animals no matter what. Unfortunately, we lost our main job due to the war. Nevertheless, we hold on and don't plan to give up. We are lucky that all our dogs were trained to ignore loud noises already before the war.

Now our dogs almost do not react to what is happening around – loud rumbles and low-flying planes. At the moment we have shelling and rockets falling close to us almost every day. We have already gotten used to feeding dogs during the ongoing fire from antiaircraft defence, automatic rifles and artillery. We hope this hell will end soon.

We now live for today only, because any break-through of Russian troops in our direction happens and we are under occupation. And now, when you are reading this article, I don't know if we are still alive or not.

Editor's note: We will endeavour to try and get copies of this year's annual sent to all of these families and our aim is to provide an update on these stories in next year's annual.

Left: Lincoln, Above right: Milly, Right: Bentley

Mirror, Mirror On The Wall...

Who is the fairest of them all? It's safe to say Lincoln, Bentley and Milly from Jimboomba, Australia are all gorgeous! This year they took part in a fabulously creative photoshoot with a mirror and we think the results are stunning! Photos kindly shared with permission from Katie Crosse of Whinny & Woof Photography.

Photographs and story by Lisa Eichman

TAVI THE COYOTE WARRIOR

True to his namesake's highlander form, McTavish (Tavi) boldly took on a coyote in his own backyard and lived to tell the tale

"I examined him and noticed a hole in his throat. My heart sunk and I screamed for my husband. We ran out of the house so fast neither of us was wearing shoes!

It was 15th July 2020 and I was watching Tavi in our backyard. He was doing his normal thing, chasing squirrels. We have two small side yards that are hard to see from my vantage point.

I was talking on the phone and he was in the side yard. I know now that I should never have taken my eyes off him. I hung up the phone and noticed his bark sounded different, then I heard a gulp. I called him and he came running back to me, mane covered in blood and barking like he was telling me a story.

I examined him and noticed a hole in his throat. My heart sunk and I screamed for my husband. We ran out of the house so fast neither of us was wearing shoes!

I wrapped a towel around his neck and put pressure on the wound. As we drove to the vet, we noticed his breathing was laboured and his tongue would not stay in his mouth. I ran into the vet and told them he was impaled by something. He was checked over and the vet wrapped his head and sent him home.

Once home we immediately knew something was not right. He was spitting up blood, his tongue was purple and his breathing was laboured. We brought him back and the vet suggested an emergency hospital.

We frantically drove about 45 minutes to our emergency vet who saved my former sheltie's life. Due to COVID, we could not go inside with Tavi so a triage nurse took him away and we cried and prayed.

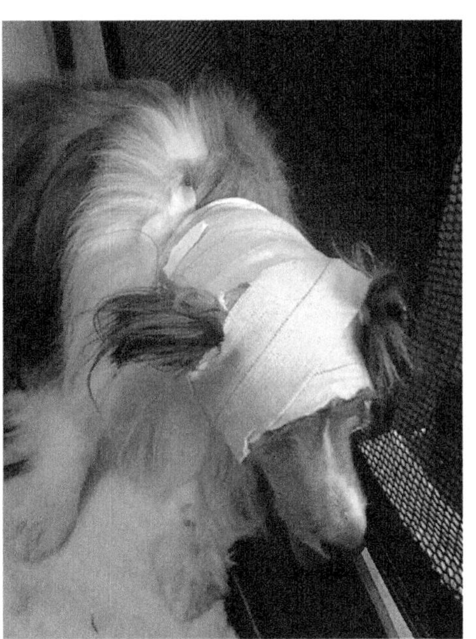

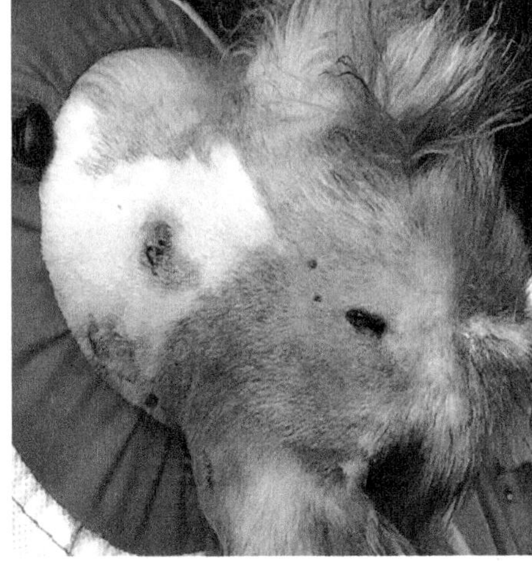

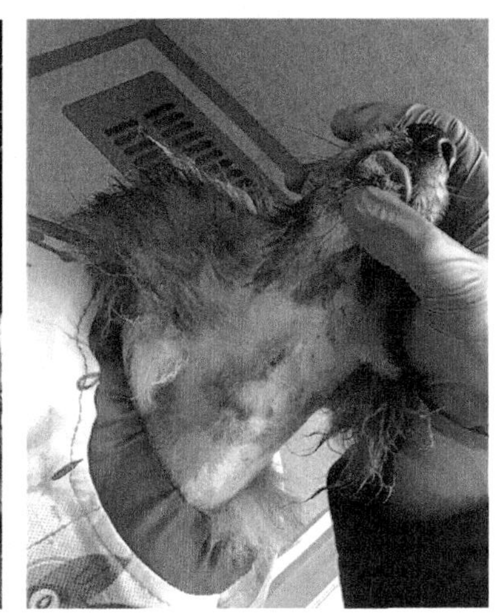

Above: Wrapped up after the first vet trip. Above right: photos from the emergency vet showing multiple bite wounds

About twenty minutes later the vet called with the news. He said Tavi had at least ten bites on his head and throat from a canine. I argued with him that it couldn't be as we saw no blood on his head. He said he was positive it was a coyote and sent me pictures because I was still in denial.

The vet assured me that Tavi would be fine in a few days. Tavi had successfully defended himself against a coyote. The vet was amazed. Tavi needed to stay for a few days in an oxygen tent and he would be fine. We left for home, stopped to get some dinner and a well-needed glass of wine, cried and prayed.

The next morning, the vet called with an update. Tavi had made it through the night and even barked at some balloons. We managed to FaceTime with Tavi. He was off oxygen, and no tracheotomy was needed. the swelling in his tongue was going down but he wasn't eating yet.

Two days later, Tavi ate on his own but threw up and it came out of the hole in his neck where he had a small oesophagal tear. The vets put a feeding tube in his neck to be used for up to two weeks. He was happy, playing with the vet staff and we were allowed to bring him home the next day.

We had feeding tube training with the vet nurses via FaceTime to let the oesophagal tear heal. The vet said he would make a full recovery and be back to his normal self in a few weeks. With our boy home, we set about coyote-proofing our yard.

Tavi was much more comfortable at home and the swelling on his neck was going down well. I made a makeshift bib with a towel and a binder clip because he had a hole under his chin to drain saliva. Sounded gross, but he was improving greatly being home and loved.

Tube feeding became a really bonding time for us all. My husband became the official blender, pharmacist and syringe loader and washer. It required a team effort as we needed to time each amount a minute apart and the whole feeding took about half an hour. And for that thirty minutes we were all totally focused on each other.

Left: our FaceTime tube feeding demonstration with the veterinary nurses.

A week after his coyote attack, Tavi was doing great. Starting to behave more like himself rolling on the rug and spending time (supervised!) out in the yard in the mornings before it got too hot. We had halved his pain medication already and were able to cut it out entirely merely a week after the attack.

We had added lots of deterrents to our yard and Tavi was feeling more confident going outside again.

The vet was pleased with his progress and decided he needed the feeding tube for ten more days but he had started playing with his toys again so must have been feeling better!

On 1st August we celebrated the last tube feeding as we reintroduced eating from a bowl. This went well for four days but we had a small setback and returned to tube feeding. The vet reassured us that tube feeding while he tries to eat is normal so we tried not to worry.

From top: tube feeding at home, swelling and bruising going down on his neck, above: starting to feel better

Right: on his beloved paddleboard again.
Bottom right: Tavi flly recovered in 2022

One month on from the attack, he was successfully eating on his own. He was getting stronger every day and we were so happy!

But at a follow-up with the vets, Tavi turned his head while the nurses were changing his bandages and the feeding tube came out. This meant he had no other option than to eat from his bowl but he was a real trooper, improving daily and continued to eat well.

Tavi was discharged from the vet at the end of August. We couldn't have been happier about his miraculous recovery. To celebrate we took him to our boat which is his favourite place. We had to promise the vet that he would not paddle board or get wet but he was so happy to be back!

Finally in early September, just 52 days after his attack, Tavi was back on his paddle board and he loved every minute of it.

Two years on, he's gone from strength to strength. His coat has grown back, he looks so regal and is in perfect health. We could never have made it through without the support of all his fans on the We Love Shelties Facebook page and we're so relieved to have our loving, happy boy back – he is a true warrior!

THE FRISBEE KID FIGHTING FIT!

At ten years old, Wee Charlie is living life to the max after his recent health scares

Hello, it's Wee Charlie here from Scotland with my annual update!

As you know from my previous story [in the 2022 Annual] I have been having 3-4 month follow-up scans on my gallbladder as sludge was found back in May last year. The specialist vets in Glasgow recommend this as shelties are at a predisposition to developing a Gallbladder Mucocole (GBM) and if left untreated can be fatal.

Since last year I have been prescribed Ursodeoxycholic (Ursodiol) which helps to keep the sludge/bile moving. Over the past few months, I have been keeping well and had my most recent gallbladder scan in Feb 2022. Thankfully it was all good news for my scan, the sludge had decreased and was very mobile, the gallbladder wall is healthy and the bile ducts were clear. The medication is doing its job, so my vet has recommended six month scans just to keep an eye on things.

During the scan, the scanner picked up something that was of concern on the lining of my stomach wall, an area of thickening/gastric mass near the bottom of my oesophagus, which was also showing something the scanner was flagging possibly as cancer. We couldn't ignore this, so we agreed with our vet the less invasive investigation for me was to have a gastrointestinal endoscopy and biopsy.

My pawrents had to leave me at the hospital overnight. It broke their hearts to go home without me and I missed them so much. During the procedure, they removed a nut kernel-type material that was lodged at the bottom of my oesophagus. More than likely something I shuffled out on a walk!

My pawrents came back the following day to pick me up and take me home, I was so pleased to see them. We are never apart, I am with my pawrents 24/7 and even go to work with them! It was an anxious four days before the results came back from the biopsies. Thankfully these surface/pinch biopsies were clear, with no cancer cells.

Because the thickening/mass in the stomach wall was deep it was advised to scan again. If this had increased in size then we would be looking at a surgical biopsy or if there was improvement to rescan again.

So five days later we went back down to Glasgow for another scan. Another anxious wait, thank goodness we got the best news

possible and it's not cancer! The gastric lesion/mass had revolved, likely was transient inflammation to the material removed during the endoscopy or possibly another unidentified reason. Even our vet was so relieved and pleased she was giving us good news as she was very nervous about the second scan after what the first scan was showing.

My pawrents and I can't thank the vets and nursing staff at VetsNow Glasgow for all the excellent care and attention they gave me during my stay at the Veterinary Hospital. But most of all I am so grateful and lucky to have the best pawrents in the world who look after me so well and give me the best life possible.

I will be eleven years old in November 2022 and I continue to enjoy my adventures out in the hills. Oh, and I LOVE my frisbee. At the beach, I am known as 'The Frisbee Kid'. I have toys galore to play with, what a happy lucky boy I am!

We are very honoured to be part of this wonderful Sheltie Annual and admire all the beautiful Shelties from all over the world, with love to you all, Wee Charlie and pawrents Linda and Ivan from St Cyrus, Aberdeenshire Scotland.

GRIFFIN'S PUPDATE ON HIS CONQUEST OF A PANCREATIC ABSCESS

Griffin's original story was printed in the 2022 I Love Shelties Annual. We told the story of his conquest of a pancreatic abscess at 11 months old with the help of the Virginia Tech (VT) Vet School in Blacksburg, VA.

His surgeon could find no reason or anything that caused this abscess and had never seen one in such a young puppy. Griffey, as he is more affectionately known, persevered through surgery, an ulcer caused by the Rimadyl (NSAID) he was on for pain and inflammation and infection that lasted for 30 days accompanied by high fevers. He was on Baytril (Enrofloxacin) and I was taking his temperature two times a day!

His journey wasn't complete in last year's annual so we wanted to share the details on his continuing journey to good health! And, one thing to note, with Covid restrictions, I was never able to accompany Griffey into the vet school. All conversations were by phone and I never saw the vets or Griffey until he was discharged.

A key date in his journey was the 11th of October 2021. It was important because it was the day his 30-day prescription for Baytril (Enrofloxacin) ended. This was the antibiotic he was on to fight the infection from the abscess. The vets at Virginia Tech told us and my local vet that if his fever spiked again, he was not to be given any more antibiotics and was to come back to them, because he might have had another abscess. This was so frightening because they never were able to determine the reason for the first abscess. On 13th October, two days after the Baytril ended, his fever spiked to 104.6 Fahrenheit (40.33 degrees Celcius)!

I called our vet and VT and they told me to get him to VT immediately. We left at 5:00 pm and arrived at VT at 7:30 pm. The emergency service admitted him and began to monitor him. They took blood work and other vitals. They called me at the hotel at 10 pm and said his temperature was down to 102.9 Fahrenheit (39.38 degrees Celcius) and his blood work had improved from the last blood work they had taken on the 3rd of September. They planned to do an ultrasound the next day and determine the next step.

The next day they called me around 1 pm and told me that his ultrasound showed a reduction in the inflammation compared to the one taken on the 3rd of September and that there was no free floating fluid in the abdominal area. This was a major improvement.

His temperature was normal, he was eating and happy. I asked them why his fever continued to spike because it was very frightening. They said his abscess was very bad and that it would take time for the inflammation to calm down. But there was no more infection, based on the blood work. They told me I should be patient and there may be occasional fever spikes until the inflammation was completely gone. I asked them if he could spend another night in their care just to make sure before I took him home.

We also made another appointment for the 8th of December for another ultrasound and blood work. The next day we came home and thankfully, there were no more fever spikes. I truly believed that he was definitely on the road to recovery and the next six weeks went well.

We returned to VT on the 8th of December. He was now under the care of the Internal Medicine Department because he was no longer an emergency admission. He had to fast from 10 pm the previous day for the blood work. Griffey vomited two times on the way down, even though he had not had any food. We arrived at 9 am, they took him in and they called around 1 pm with both good and bad news.

The good news was that the ultrasound was normal. The radiologist told me that if he had not done ultrasounds four times on Griffey, he would have thought this was a completely different dog! He was thrilled that Griffey's ultrasound was normal. But the blood work was not normal. Griffey's Triglyceride level was 2610 (normal is a range of 23-143) and his cholesterol was 604 (normal is a range of 129-332)!

They asked me if I was sure I fasted him and I told them I did. We went to bed at 10 pm, he sleeps in bed with us and I put him in the car at 7 am. He did not eat anything. So we decided that he should spend the night at VT and they would repeat the blood work in the morning. They repeated the blood work.

The levels were lower, but still too high. Triglycerides were 975 and Cholesterol was 551. They prescribed Fenofibrate 200mg, they told me it would bring down both levels and that it is a very safe drug for long-term use. Since that time, I have learned that many of my friends take Fenofibrate and have taken it for years which helped me stop worrying. We made an appointment for a follow-up to see the effect of the Fenofibrate.

On the 13th of January, we arrived at VT at 4 pm. We decided to have him stay the night so we could ensure that he fasted properly and they took blood in the morning. His Triglyceride level was 81—well within normal range! His Cholesterol level was 288, again, well within normal range. The vets were very pleased and felt comfortable discharging him to our local vet, knowing that they would call if they needed help with Griffey.

It was a happy new year! I'm writing this now at the end of March 2022 and Griffey continues to do well. We are thrilled!

NOTE: Griffey's case was so unique that the Vet School Director decided to use his story to highlight the emergency department and its work. VT is planning a major renovation and expansion and Griffey's story was the one they chose for their promotion which was amazing!

Mila Flo and Pearl from the UK

HYDRO GIRL

> ***"When I arrived, I immediately knew something was wrong [and] I knew she would have to come home with me.***

Photos and story by Barbara Mariz

Three years ago, I embarked on one of the most difficult but rewarding journeys of my life: rescuing a disabled puppy. Well, at the moment, I had no real sense of the gravity of her situation.

I remember seeing a post online for a 9-week-old Shetland Sheepdog. The owner noticed that she was not behaving like a traditional puppy and was going to return her to the breeder. When I say I wasted no time in contacting both the owner and breeder to take her, I mean NO time.

Most often, sick or disabled puppies are euthanized young. Within a day, I found myself driving three hours to pick this puppy up with my two shelties, Max and Sophie in tow.

When I arrived, I immediately knew something was wrong: she had a large, apple-like head with soft spots; she was walking in circles; she was running into objects and she did not want to be near people. I knew she would have to come home with me. Upon visiting my local veterinary, he suspected hydrocephalus.

This is a condition where cerebrospinal fluid builds up inside the city of the brain. This accumulation of fluid leads to increased brain pressure and significant damage. My veterinarian gave her another month to live, seeing how severe her condition was.

In a state of despair, I begged him for options and was referred to a neurologist. Through imaging studies and a physical exam, the doctor confirmed her hydrocephalus and said she had a poor prognosis. However, he agreed to treat her with some standard medications. I truly believe he saved Emma's life. I am so very happy to say she is now three years old and surpassed all odds.

Emma has many clinical symptoms of hydrocephalus:

- She is untrainable: Emma still wears diapers as she cannot be potty trained
- She has visual deficits and down and out gaze, also called sunsetting
- She also had a large head with soft spots (thankfully they closed)
- She has extremely abnormal behaviour-hypersensitive to touch, sounds, motion and excitable, inappropriate vocalization, increased aggression and spinning/circling
- She walks with an abnormal gait; it can vary from prance-like to unsteady

Even though Emma has many difficulties and is a handful, she exceeds expectations every day. She is happy and currently pain-free.

Emma is an integral part of my family; actually, the heart of it. We never know how long we will have with her, but we cherish every day and give her the best of ourselves. I wouldn't give her up for the world.

I am also grateful to all the friends who have supported her and our family along the way. She has changed me into a more patient and empathic human, and I love my little hydro warrior.

A SHELTIE FOR ALL SEASONS

We've gathered together some of the most spectacular shots of our sheltie friends enjoying seasonal weather around the globe. I'm sure you can agree that a sheltie by your side looks good in all weathers!

Shanel, 1 in the cherry blossom in Le Thor, France

Humphrey (left) and Lotus (right) in the daffodils in Norfolk, UK

Miss Tallahassee stopping to sniff the spring flowers in Dorset, UK

Freya, 2 in the bluebells, Kent, UK

Top right: Jordie from New Zealand,

Rght: Bonnie, 2 from Perth, UK

Clockwise from top left: Bryn, Charli and Jordie from New Zealand, Finn, 4 from Dunedin, New Zealand, Joy, 3 from Norfolk, UK, Keeko, 7 from Arbroath, UK

Above: L to R: Bramble, Ben and Rosie from Norfolk, UK

Right: Mila Flo and Pearl from the UK and Daisy, 11 from Bath, UK

Clockwise from top left: Teddy (left) and Ollie (right) enjoying the summer sun in Helsby, UK.

Our favourite Sheltie mix Laddie chilling by the pool in Greenwood, Arkansas, USA

Layla and Levi keeping cool in Arkansas, USA

Teddy the lifesaver in Norfolk, UK

Top: Wee Charlie, 10 from Aberdeenshire Scotland

Middle left: Luna, 4 from Carmarthen, UK

Middle right: Charli from New Zealand

Left: Maya, 20 months from Carmarthen, UK

Clockwise from top: Talia, 3, Teddy, 3 and Mia, 7 from Norfolk, UK. Biscuit from Ontario, Canada. Bonnie, 2 from Perth, UK. Finn, 4 and Laddie, 1 from Dunedin, New Zealand

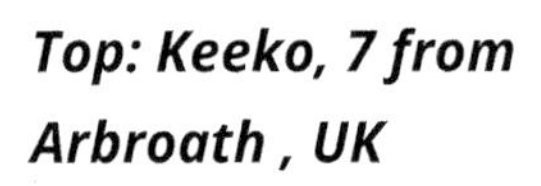

Top: Keeko, 7 from Arbroath , UK

Middle: Reglisse, 2 from France.

Right: Fizz, 13 from Kent, UK

Facing page: Shanel, 1 from Le Thor, France

Top left: Teddy (left) and Ollie (right) enjoying the autumn sun in Helsby, UK

Top right: Aline from Budapest, Hungary

Middle Left: Daisy, 11 from Bath, UK

Middle Right: Wee Charlie, 10 from Aberdeenshire Scotland

Left: Cali, 3 in the autumn leaves in Berkshire, UK

Lucius, ***Lucky-Luke Star Nature Dark Eastern***, 1 from Hungary

Above: Finn, 4 and Laddie, 1 from Dunedin, New Zealand

Below clockwise from top left: Biscuit from Ontario, Canada, Aline from Budapest, Hungary, Bryn from New Zealand, sheltie mix Laddie from Greenwood, Arkansas, USA

Top: Mila Flo and Pearl keeping clean in their coats from the autumn mud in the UK

Above: Charli in the New Zealand heather

Left: Breccan, 5 from Ohio, USA

Clockwise from top left: Biscuit from Ontario, Canada, Aline from Budapest, Hungary, Chester on a lovely frosty morning, Bellshill UK, Blossom from Lincolnshire UK, Humphrey from Norfolk, UK

Top: Shanel, 1 from Le Thor, France

Above: Gracie from North Carolina, USA

Above centre: Daisy, 11 from Bath, UK

Above right: Keeko, 7 from Arbroath , UK

Right: Wee Charlie, 10 from Aberdeenshire Scotland

SHELTIE CELEBRATIONS

Shelties are such great posers and love to get involved in everything we do... that includes celebrating throughout the year!

Breccan the birthday boy!

Badger, 1 from Cambridgeshire UK

Dusty from Arkansas, USA

Gracie getting her therapy licence from North Carolina, USA

The Sunshine State Shelties and Circa the cat ready for Easter

Little Leprechaun's!

Ready for Fourth July!

Joy celebrating the Queen's Platinum Jubilee!

Mia, Teddy and Talia's Platinum Jubilee celebration

Dex is ready for Halloween!

Picardy, Echo and Encore trick or treating!

A VERY SHELTIE CHRISTMAS

Above: Picardy, Echo and Encore from Centerville, Ohio, USA

Top left: Riley,Chester and Bailey impatiently waiting for Santa Bellshill UK

Left: Blossom from Lincolnshire UK

Top: Talia, 3, Teddy, 3 and Mia, 7 from Norfolk, UK

Above: Mila Flo and Pearl from the UK

Left: Badger, 1 from Cambridgeshire UK

Christmas Artwork of Mia, Teddy and Talia (Shelties By The Sea) by Camilla Fellas Arnold

Clockwise from top left: Chip from Fort Worth, Texas, USA, Aline from Budapest, Hungary, Picardy, Echo and Encore from Centerville, Ohio, USA, Lucy, 10, from North Carolina, USA

Top left and right: Bonnie, 2 from Perth, UK. Above left: Dusty from Arkansas, USA. Above right: Dex, 13, from California, USA

Shanel, 1 from Le Thor, France

OUR SHELTIE CHRISTMAS TRADITION

Images courtesy of Rob Banbury, story by Joe and Melody Cheal

In 2007, we asked an illustrator friend of ours, Rob Banbury, to draw a few cartoon pictures of our shelties. From this, we commissioned him to do us a Christmas card. Initially, we liked the idea of sending a personalised picture. Something a bit different, a bit silly, that would accompany an equally silly newsletter!

However, over the years, the pictures have become a story (and a history) of our lives with the most wonderful creatures on earth, but then… doesn't everyone with shelties feel the same way? The adventures of Remus and Buck (or 'Buck and Remus' as Buck would have it) became immortalised through these fantastic illustrations.

The first one (above) saw Buck (tricolour) and Remus (shaded sable) attempting to pull a cracker which reflected their occasional tug-of-war games. Indeed, they had a strange way of fetching toys that had been thrown – Remus would run and pick it up, with Buck shouting in his ear. Remus would then bring the item back and drop it just out of reach. Buck's duty was then to pick it up and bring it to us!

'NOT A CREATURE WAS STIRRING - NOT EVEN A MOUSE!'

The pictures then became more detailed like this one from 2008. Remus had many nicknames, but the one that stuck was 'Mouse'.

The year we moved into a house called Woodpeckers.

When we discovered that Buck loved to fetch ring-shaped frisbees!

When Buck discovered a penchant for fish food.

When Remus dug the one and only hole in his lifetime.

And when they chased croquet balls (which added a new dimension to the game) and chased herons away from the fish pond. This is just a selection from the years and times and of course things change. We now have a new sheltie family but perhaps that might be the subject for another year!

THE MAGNIFICENT SEVEN

In this two part story, Jo Austin shares how a very large litter caused so much worry but ultimately led to lasting love.

Angel allowed us the good grace to eat our evening meal, as Jennifer recalls, sausage and mash, one of our family favourites, so that we were suitably sustained ahead of the mammoth task of helping her to deliver her puppies.

The last mouthfuls of food were hastily consumed as Angel's appearance indicated that the arrival of puppies was imminent. We were expecting six, possible seven, puppies in this litter. The number had been highlighted a few weeks previously during an ultrasound scan at the vet. Angel's first litter of four puppies was more average for a sheltie so the vet's discovery of six or seven in this litter was quite a surprise.

We placed our empty plates on the counter in the kitchen and returned to the lounge to witness Angel straining to deliver the first puppy. Seconds later, puppy one arrived in the world. It was 18.23 on Friday 6th May 2013

Puppy one, a tri-coloured male, was diligently cleaned and warmed by Angel. She was an absolute natural when it came to whelping and raising puppies. Angel was a dedicated and nurturing mummy to her babies. The puppies arrived in quick succession and Angel lovingly attended to each of them with little assistance from me or Jennifer. Once she'd attended to each puppy, we placed them gently in a nearby box surrounded by towels and a hot water bottle for warmth. Angel could then concentrate her efforts on delivering the next baby.

That first puppy we named Onyx. Puppy two followed Onyx at 18.48, a blue merle male, the biggest of the litter who we named Ernie. He would later earn his nickname of 'the fat pasty'.

Puppy three arrived very quickly after Ernie and was another tri-coloured male. Born at 18.54 this puppy was named Jax, soon discovered to be the most laid-back lad of the litter. At 19.10 our little girl arrived, a very petite tri-colour puppy who Jennifer named Millie. Jennifer got to name this one as she would be the puppy that Angel and I gifted to her.

After Millie, puppy number five arrived. This puppy was to set our hearts racing. Puppy five was delivered after a bit of a break for Angel. He arrived at 20.17. Angel stood to deliver him, she had laid down for the first four puppies, so I cupped my hands to soften his drop. As Angel delivered him into my hands I gasped and exclaimed, 'oh, he's so tiny,' The puppy was at least half the size of all his litter mates. Not only was he tiny but he was also not breathing.

I wrapped him in a towel and gently but frantically rubbed him all over. I presented him to Angel so that she would lick him and hoped that her licking, and my massage, would stimulate his little heart and lungs. It felt surreal, a bit like the moment in 101 Dalmatians where they thought a puppy hadn't survived. Thankfully, just like in the Disney movie, Tiny took his first breath. It was clear that Tiny was very weak.

After Tiny, puppy six, Aree, another blue merle male arrived at 20.37. After some time passed, we assumed that Angel had finished delivering her babies as there was no more straining and she appeared calm and at rest.

I began to help Angel to clean herself a bit and lifted her tail for one last check. I was startled to see one more puppy laying quietly and keeping warm beneath her beautiful fluffy tail. I guess he was so warm and cosy there, so he remained quiet as a mouse until we discovered him. We took his birth time as that moment, 21.24. He was Angel's seventh and final puppy, another blue merle male. Seven is a lucky number for us as a family. We weren't sure there would be a seventh puppy though, so we named him Lucky.

Seven beautiful puppies were born that evening. All seven survived but we knew there would be difficult times ahead as Tiny, our preemie pup, was very, very poorly. Millie was the only girl in such a big Sheltie litter. She had six brothers to look out for her though and, as it turned out, they did just that. She turned out to be the best Sheltie sister too though.

RAISING TINY

At 100g, Tiny from the Magnificent Seven litter was dangerously small. Could Jo Austin and her family save him?

Our preemie puppy, Tiny, couldn't suckle from his mum, Angel. So we began the marathon task of hand-rearing him. If he had any chance of surviving, this was the only way. While Angel fed her other six puppies and settled for sleep, we prepared puppy formula and sterilised puppy feeding equipment.

I fed Tiny myself initially and then other family members learned this vital skill to help. Tiny initially needed a two hourly feeding schedule so we knew that more helpers would be useful, especially as I got very little sleep. The fact is, we all fell in love with Tiny from his first dramatic moment of birth. We would have done whatever was needed to help him.

As it transpired, Tiny couldn't even suckle from a puppy feeding bottle at first either, he was so weak. Instead, I had to feed him his formula with the smallest size syringe. This method of feeding requires a slow and steady hand. There can be no rushing, patience is vital with syringe feeding to avoid any chance of the puppy aspirating the milk into their delicate lungs. This would have catastrophic repercussions. Tiny was fed very slowly with very small amounts of formula every two hours, or earlier if he woke crying. He had to be held gently but firmly to keep him upright too. It was a fine balancing act with a tiny, squirming puppy.

I dutifully and lovingly fed Tiny two hourly for two whole weeks. As others, such as my children, learned the art of syringe feeding they were able to help during the daytime.

Each night Tiny slept beside me in a washing-up bowl filled with small blankets, towels, a cuddly toy and hot water bottles.

After each feed, the hot water bottles were refreshed to keep them warm enough for him. Newborn puppies, like humans, cannot regulate their body temperature and can become chilled all too quickly. This is the reason why puppies sleep in a puppy pile and with their mother to keep each other warm with their body heat. Tiny couldn't sleep with his litter mates and his mum though as he was at far too great a risk of suffocation.

Hand-rearing a puppy takes a great amount of dedication. It was exhausting. But as all three of my children were still living at home at that time, they all pitched in to help. They didn't just help Tiny, they helped me and the whole litter. They also helped with the everyday running of the house. Raising Tiny became a team effort and the Austin team became the A-team!

The litter soon became known among family, friends, and the sheltie world as the 'Magnificent 7'. They were all truly beautiful, a wonderful litter and they remain my favourite litter to this day.

Remarkably, Tiny began to grow a little bit each day. Although far behind his litter mates in size, they were no match for him in personality. It quickly became clear that, despite many setbacks and health issues, Tiny was a brave warrior. He fought and fought. He was equally as determined to live as we were for him. In the early days, he was weighed twice a day, so we could determine his progress. All the while he was gaining weight, we knew we were heading in the right direction.

During the daytime, we all took turns to keep him warm. We would carry him in our dressing gowns, in hoodies and pockets. Sometimes we even carried him in our bras – except Robert that is! We had to keep him warm and body heat was the best way.

We placed Tiny in the puppy pile during the day at times when someone was available to keep watch. This helped him to form and overwhelmingly heart-warming to witness as she would often sit at my feet and lay her face in my lap, close to Tiny, as I fed him. What a truly special relationship we shared.

The vets checked on Tiny very often in his first weeks of life. One vet had said that if Tiny made it to two weeks old then he might just be in with a chance of surviving. When two weeks came and Tiny was still with us we celebrated with a bottle of champagne that we were saving. Tiny was worth celebrating.

At two and half weeks old Tiny suddenly started to pass a great deal of blood with his stools. We rushed him back to the vet. He was given lots of medication. This little puppy gave us so many scares in those first few weeks. Each time his resilience, strength and clear love of life helped him to pull through. He

maintain a bond with his litter mates and his mum. At birth, Tiny weighed just 100g. It's amazing to recall that he was half the size and weight of the next smallest litter mate. Angel clearly understood and accepted that she couldn't care for this puppy. But she trusted me and the children with his care. It was

recovered from this setback and my breaking heart and rising blood pressure were given the green light to return to normal again.

Then shockingly, at three weeks old he began to deteriorate again. He developed what breeders call 'swollen belly syndrome.' We

were horrified to see his little tummy swell up so big and at the same time all his fur fell out. He became all scaly and scabby with little sores on his body. Very few puppies survive swollen belly syndrome. Our hearts were breaking.

We researched as much as we could and spoke to vets and other breeders about their experience with this dire health issue. We could find no one who understood what causes it or what it really is. All we could do was continue to offer intensive, loving care to Tiny.

Yet again Tiny demonstrated his warrior personality. He fought and fought. He was one very determined little puppy. He would not give up and neither would we. Surprisingly, Tiny's health improved dramatically at weaning time.

Although he learnt to stand on his legs at the same time as the other puppies, he was a very wobbly little fellow. He and his litter mates were first weaned on Weetabix mixed with puppy formula milk. They later transitioned to puppy weaning meat.

Tiny belly-flopped into the first plate of Weetabix. He sprawled like an upside down snow angel, face first leaving no room for his litter mates to share the food. After this moment he went from strength to strength. As an adult dog, Tiny grew into one of the largest shelties we have produced. He is also one of the healthiest. He can eat anything whereas many shelties have very delicate stomachs.

A hand-reared puppy is a very special puppy indeed. There's a tight bond, a closeness that just can't be described. Having that special relationship meant that it became impossible for us to consider parting with him. So while his litter mates moved to their forever families, Tiny was never sold. He remained in the care of our family.

HERE COMES TROUBLE!

Shelties, what are they like?! Have a laugh at some of the funniest photos we received and see what this cheeky lot have been doing this year!

Blaze was so hungry he decided to eat a table!

Wee Charlie, was caught snooping for snacks!

Laddie took up driving lessons

Mila Flo and Pearl make a rather damp trio

'Geronimo!' Maya, 20 months from Carmarthen, UK

Bonnie, didn't think much of her new toy

Layla thought the lollipop looked tasty!

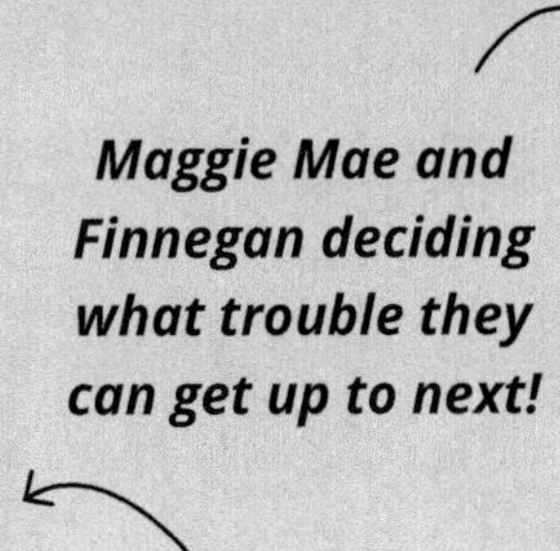

Maggie Mae and Finnegan deciding what trouble they can get up to next!

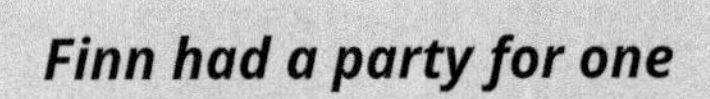

Finn had a party for one

Halo and Millie decided to go on their own holiday

Duskie would quite like some more ice cream thanks!

Sir Tavish has a penchant for sitting on tables....

And the occasional basket!

RUAIRI'S GREAT ESCAPE

Ruairi had been a bit of a handful as a puppy. He was very independent with a strong prey drive, chasing anything that moved. He was a real show-off with other dogs through adolescence but settled into the perfect dog by three and half years old and began winning his way through obedience competitions. As he got older we bonded and had a really strong connection.

A few years later I boarded two of my shelties, Piper and Ruairi (then 6) while I went on holiday to South Africa. I awoke halfway through the holiday with a nightmare that Ruairi had escaped the kennels. I told my roommate about the nightmare the following morning and she said I was just missing my dogs but it felt so real to me.

When I got home I went straight to my back gate half expecting Ruairi to be lying there, which of course, he wasn't. I phoned a friend who was looking after my puppy Moray and asked if she'd been contacted by the kennel whilst I was away. She laughed, telling me not to be so silly and that Ruairi would be so excited to see me when I picked him up the next day.

Arriving at the kennels, the owner gave me a wry smile and said, "you didn't tell me shelties can jump!" Ruairi had somehow climbed two 6-foot chain link fences and was hiding in the corner of a field of sheep. She had taken food and my other sheltie, Piper into the field and with a bit of perseverance, eventually caught him. But when she brought him out of the kennels, he jumped in the car and turned his back on me. It took a couple of days before he'd have anything to do with me and I didn't dare let him off the lead for a week!

I used to work in boarding kennels so I know that some dogs can be climbers, poodles and terriers are especially good at it. I never expected it from a sheltie but a lesson learned – never underestimate your dog! I still count my blessings we had a good outcome. I now use the services of a dog sitter and haven't boarded my dogs since!

Anne Smith, Bedlington, UK

Photographs and story by Elizabeth Wright

CLARA'S ALL CLEAR

A weepy eye and an overbite caused Clara a whole host of problems all before she had even turned one!

After our beloved sheltie, Heidi died, our home was not the same. So we began to look for a sheltie pup to help fill the gap Heidi had left. I joined forums online and everyone was so helpful! After a couple of months, we found a lady called Ann whose sheltie was expecting.

We were so excited when the news came that she had a pup for us. It was a long wait, but Ann kept us updated with progress. Soon we were making the trip from Northamptonshire to Herefordshire to meet Clara and bring her home to her new family in July.

She was such a happy little thing, so full of energy and very cheeky! However, after a couple of weeks with us, we noticed that her eye was very weepy and conjunctivitis was diagnosed and treated.

In October, I noticed that she seemed to be taking a long time to eat and that she was developing a bit of an overbite. When I looked closely, I could see her canines were starting to dig into her palate so an operation was quickly arranged to remove her baby canine teeth.

Several vet visits later, we were referred to a canine dentist in Cambridge. The vet was excellent. He confirmed that her overbite was significant and that her lower canines would continue to cause problems and infections.

We agreed that we shouldn't remove them as that risks breaking the jaw, so instead, we attempted extensions, a type of doggy brace, which would push the canines wide and not up into her palate. But after a long operation, unfortunately, the dog braces didn't work.

Our second option was to reduce the canines by cutting them down. Another operation and visits ensued. Fortunately, this was successful, but she may need root canal treatment in the future.

However, whilst she was seeing the vets regularly, the eye problem flared up from time to time. Our vets thought it could be microphthalmia (an unusually small eyeball). Whilst rare, it is something to which shelties can be prone. We were advised to wait until she was fully grown and then there could be surgery to address the issue.

But Clara's right eye grew worse and was closed much of the time. We couldn't wait until she was fully mature, so went back to the vets again. They referred us to a Canine Ophthalmic specialist in Bedfordshire, who diagnosed Distichiasis – where eyelashes grow in the wrong place, turning in towards the eye. This meant another operation to have electrolysis and the follicles frozen, which can be risky if the tear ducts get damaged.

Fortunately, it seems to have worked, and whilst she may need further operations in the future, we know that she is comfortable and despite her young age hasn't had any adverse reactions to her four general anaesthetics.

Clara turned one in June 2022. She is now excelling at obedience training and has just passed her Bronze Kennel Club Good Citizen Award. She's had a lot of problems but remains happy and is loving life. We hope that we won't be needing so many vet trips from now on!

During the insurance process, we had to get her records from the vet to forward them on. In the middle of all the Latin and dates, we saw a comment that made us smile; "super wriggly and very happy girl that loves a biscuit!" which sums her up for us!

GRANDAD KNOWS BEST

At 85, Eric now has dementia but told this story in his own words recounting how one suggestion about getting a sheltie for his granddaughter changed the family's lives forever

Above left: Eric with Lassie and right: Camilla, Carly and Eric.
Facing page: Eric and Teddy. Below: Camilla and Lassie.

I remember my granddaughter Camilla asking for a puppy when she was seven. A sheltie came straight to my mind because I use to go to Great Yarmouth Dog Training Club. There were two shelties at the club and I thought to myself they were lovely little dogs, perfect for Camilla, I thought to myself.

The family started a hunt for a sheltie and we were lucky enough to find one thirteen miles from home. A week later we went to see the two puppies and Camilla chose her first sheltie pup who she called Lassie.

Each week Camilla would bring Lassie along with me to the dog training club and did very well in obedience. We use to spend our weekends travelling all over Norfolk to obedience & fun dog shows, where Lassie and Camilla got 49 rosettes and 2 trophies together. Sadly, Lassie got bowel cancer and passed away when she was ten.

A year later my daughter Jeanette and Camilla got another sheltie. This time we travelled to Ely in Cambridgeshire and got Carly. Again, Camilla would come to obedience classes with me.

One of my best memories of Carly was when I was taken to the hospital for a knee replacement. Jeanette would wheel me in a wheelchair outside and Camilla would be waiting with Carly. Carly would sit on my lap while I was pushed around the hospital grounds in my wheelchair.

Then came the announcement that Camilla was going to get married and her then-fiancé asked Jeanette what was going to happen with Carly. Jeanette said 'you're taking my daughter you can't have Carly as well'.

Left: a day out with Talia as a puppy and above: winter walks with puppy Teddy and Carly

It was decided we would get a sheltie for a wedding gift, so Mia arrived. Mia has done really well, she did some obedience training and then started agility. I used to enjoy watching Camilla work Mia and going to agility shows.

Then Teddy came along to join Mia. Teddy is special as he's the first boy we've had, he's always pleased to see and greet everyone. Teddy lives up to his name Richmaus Yogi because he's always looking for an adventure!

Shortly after Teddy arrived, we lost Carly to a seizure. I remember the day I was with her when she had her first and also her last seizure. It was horrible to witness.

Jeanette now has Talia who is three years old and the fifth sheltie I've had the pleasure of knowing. Shelties are the most loyal companion.

Now I look after Talia in the evening and she looks after me. I love it when Mia and Teddy come to visit me and I watch them play with Talia. I love going on walks with Mia, Teddy and Talia, especially to Fairhaven Woodland Water Garden. And it's always great fun when we go to Doggie Diner in Cromer together.

My only regret is that I never actually owned a sheltie myself but I have been blessed to have seen five little beauties.

Clockwise from top left: enjoying days out in summer 2022 with Talia, Teddy and Mia, dressing as Field Marshal Montgomery with Mia and a vintage BSA, visitng a 1940s cafe with Teddy and reading the 2022 I Love Shelties Annual with Teddy, Talia and Mia

SHELTIES IN DISGUISE

What a sheltie won't do for a treat – even if it means dressing up in some crazy outfits so mum can get a photo!

Todd trying out his fairy wings!

Badger keeping warm in his Christmas jumper

Dex keeping dry in his raincoat

Chip looking dashing in his tartan hat

Shanel ready for the masquerade ball!

Will the judge find Zorro guilty of being too darn cute? Courtesy of Rebecca Reed Photography

Ahoy me hearties! says Ellie

Dally is pretty as a princess

Is it Frankenstein or is it Pippin?

Mila Flo and Pearl the ghostly ghouls (girls!)

Picardy, Echo and Encore bringing the magic

Mac is suited up and ready to go!

SHELTIES IN DISGUISE

Check out Breccan in his many disguises!

Biscuit and Cricket doing some modelling for their upcoming album cover artwork!

Dory (*Calistros Forget Me Not*), 4, from Hampshire, UK

sweet ROAM

My Czechoslovakian Boy; Worth The Wait

Like with so many others, post-pandemic lockdown altered my way of working and eventually one of my three jobs ended completely. This meant I had a lot more time, particularly on evenings and weekends. I could now get back into training my dogs as things started to open up, attending classes and shows, something which had not been possible for a long time.

In February 2020 I acquired a young tri-colour bitch. She came to me having had no socialisation or real-life opportunities; she was wary of everything. Once she had settled in nicely, I began to train her and the old buzz started to return.

With re-kindled enthusiasm, I started to think about getting a puppy, a bitch puppy, who would hopefully go on to produce future Torriglen Shelties. My line had sadly come to an end when I was widowed. I had plenty of time, there was no rush, so I started window shopping for a kennel whose stock appealed to me.

There wasn't a lot happening. Litters were scarce owing to the travel restrictions, but I had been particularly taken with what I had seen of Bohemia Classic. I had seen many of

"I couldn't stop thinking about his cute little face looking out of the pictures at me... Then the sensible voice came back, "How do you expect to pay for this puppy? You have no money saved!!!"

their posts on Facebook. At first, I hadn't realised they lived in the Czech Republic. They, in turn, had no idea who I was. So when I made contact with them to express my interest in owning a puppy from them, I was understandably told that first, they would need to know a lot more about me. Having explained my long involvement in shelties and discovering we had a mutual friend I was accepted.

Milan and Tatjana breed shelties in three colours though I was particular in wanting a sable bitch. Tatjana mentioned that they had a lovely sable litter, all boys and although they had another litter due, they were also hoping to keep a bitch from that litter should there be something nice. She sent me photos of the boys, which I had already seen on Facebook, but I reiterated I wasn't in any hurry and it really was a bitch I was interested in having.

I looked at the photos and reflected on our conversation. One of the puppies had caught my eye. Over the next few days, I thought about him a lot but always dismissed the thoughts of him because he was a dog not a bitch, AND I wasn't ready for a puppy yet.

🐾 🐾 🐾 🐾 🐾 🐾 🐾 🐾 🐾 🐾 🐾 🐾 🐾 🐾

Another voice in my head spoke of how well partnerships with my boys had been in the past, teaming up with good all-rounders across several disciplines. I had found, that though my girls were good, the true commitment came from the boys. I couldn't stop thinking about his cute little face looking out of the pictures at me. Why not go for a dog while I was currently in no position to breed? Then the sensible voice came back, "How do you expect to pay for this puppy? You have no money saved!!!"

Days passed. I saw more pictures on Facebook of the litter but now only one puppy was un-reserved – my puppy! I told a friend how I was wrangling with my thoughts. I had even set his picture as a wallpaper on my phone! My friend told me if I was serious then I would need to act fast as there had been so much interest in the litter.

Next thing I was reserving him with no idea how on earth I was going to pay for him. The one advantage with him being overseas meant he couldn't leave until he was fully vaccinated against rabies. The earliest he could travel would be 16 weeks old. I started to raise the funds.

I remember my frantic efforts to scrape the money together. I sold clothes, jewellery, scrap metal and pet portraits. I was surprised with a little determination by how easy it was. I paid for my puppy, who I decided to call Blaze on account of him being born an Aries, a fire sign.

Next, we started to talk about how to get him to me in Scotland. That part turned out to be a logistical nightmare. Apart from the pandemic making things awkward, Brexit had also happened. Couriers that were familiar with Milan and Tatjana had not renewed their European licences. Many couriers were making long-distance treks across Europe with huge vans. We didn't want this for Blaze and a flight option was way beyond my means.

Milan was prepared to drive him over himself but discovered only licensed couriers were allowed to bring an animal into the UK. For that same reason, I couldn't collect him myself. Plans were made and plans were broken again.

I decided it would probably be easier to arrange to drop him off nearer London than Perthshire so arranged with a Czech courier to deliver to coincide with my staying with family in Harwich. I booked my annual leave and drove down only to be told the courier had been forced to change the dates of departure to accommodate another dog. I returned home without Blaze; it was all becoming very depressing. I feared Milan and Tatjana would be regretting selling me the pup. Milan offered to refund my money if I wanted as the situation seemed impossible. I knew I definitely did not want that as I already loved the pup I had yet to meet.

Finally, a solution was found. A friend in London offered to have Blaze delivered to her where he could spend a few days there to recover from the journey, then her husband would drive halfway to meet me. I could hardly contain myself. I met Blaze in person at Tebay services. He was finally here!

Blaze and I bonded immediately, he is very smart and I'm sure we will have a lot of fun competing together. I am a believer in fate and that somehow a puppy that was born thousands of miles away was destined to be by my side.

Story by Louise Saunders

This is Tse, *Aucanada Go For Gold* a male bi-blue from Mallorca. He is now 11.5 months old (5.5 months in the photo) and is hoping to be an agility dog one day. He is the happiest dog and is so open and friendly with everyone he meets. He loves to run and fills every day with so much joy!

MISS TALLAHASSEE VINTAGE FASHIONISTA

Miss Tallahassee's owner loves dressing in 1950's vintage style and makes matching coats for Miss Tallahassee. They turn heads and bring smiles to everyone who sees them and we can certainly see why!

Every vintage lady needs a leopard print coat!

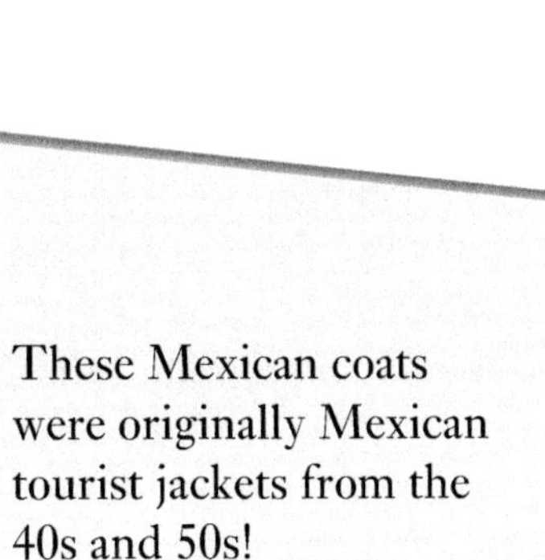

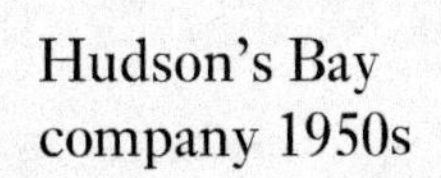

Hudson's Bay company 1950s

Matching coat made from a 1940s blanket!

These Mexican coats were originally Mexican tourist jackets from the 40s and 50s!

Photos and story by Yvette Tinlin

NEVER WITHOUT A SHELTIE

It was back in 1995 and I was recovering following a serious accident – I'd been in hospital for nearly a year and was only just learning to walk again. My last few weeks in the hospital were spent looking through dog breed books, my greatest wish was that I would get a puppy once I got out, to cheer me up in ways only a dog can.

I'd been brought up with a Rough Collie, and then two German Shepherds. However, I knew that due to the frail state I was in, a big dog would just knock me over. I was looking at smaller breeds to get some ideas, the obvious ones being Poodles and King Charles Spaniels. I'd never heard of Shetland Sheepdogs.

One day I was reading OK! Magazine, catching up on celebrity gossip, not thinking about puppy possibilities when out fell an insert for pedigree chum and my life changed forever. The advert showed a picture of a recent Crufts winner; *Myriehewe Rosa Bleu*. I could see the size was exactly what I was looking for and the look of the dog was completely in line with the bigger dogs I'd always loved but in a smaller package.

I was hooked. I looked up Shetland Sheepdogs in my dog breed books and saw they had all the qualities I was after. My next purchase was the book *Shetland Sheepdogs* by Jan Moody which I read cover to cover and it remains my sheltie bible. I was now ready for my search to begin as soon as I could get out of hospital.

I went to see a litter down in Horsham which was an absolute joy, but they decided to keep the girl we were looking at – I was gutted.

Facing page: Purdey
Below: Purdey meeting Harry

> **"What does one do in this kind of situation?**
>
> **Get another puppy to fill the family home with joy, of course!**

A puppy in Chertsey became available, but from the Callart line and on a breeding contract. I had to wait till Olwen Gwynne-Jones had seen her to decide if she wanted her. I waited with bated breath, but then received the news that Olwen had thought she'd be too big.

We immediately rushed down to see her. We fell completely in love and I couldn't wait to bring her home in a couple of weeks. We decided to call her Purdey (*Lythe of Spirit*). I'd watched all episodes of The New Avengers during my hospital stay, so she was named after Joanna Lumley's character.

She was a wonderful dog. In her early days, we were living with my mum and dad during the week, moving back to my flat with my fiancé at the weekends. I always had to have someone around to help me and was still using crutches to walk around the house and a wheelchair for going out. It was hard for me both physically and mentally but this little bundle of joy could always make me smile and keep going. My fiancé had never had a pet of any kind before but within weeks, Purdey had completely won him over and he was besotted.

By the time she was a year old, we'd moved back to our flat in Chiswick full time. I could walk further unaided and we had a small garden she could play in. Then at the end of 1996, we got married and moved to Berkshire. We had a much bigger indoor space, garden and lovely walks right on our doorstep.

My mum and dad moved so they could be nearer to us and I went back to work. Purdey was always with one of us, I don't think she was ever left alone for more than two hours. The years passed by very happily.

Sadly I lost my mum and dad in 2003 and 2004. I was distraught and Purdey was now without her second family, so what does one do in this kind of situation? Get another puppy to fill the family home with joy, of course!

Above: Harry (left) and Emma (right)

Our new search began. I was looking for another girl as I'd never had a male dog and wanted to stick with what I knew. Then two litters came up at once. We booked to see both on the same day. One had a tricolour bitch available and the other had three dogs; two of which were tricolour and one shaded sable. I was positive we'd be going for the girl who we were seeing first, but the boys happened to live very close to us so we decided we may as well go to see them on our way home.

That was when we first met *Shady Pines Little Drummer Boy*, later to be known as Harry. He stole our hearts from the second we saw him, leaving his brothers to come and sit in my husband's hand the whole time we were there. It was as if he was telling us he was our dog. That was it, he was definitely the one.

We couldn't wait for him to come home and introduce him to Purdey. As the wonderful natured dog she'd always been, she welcomed him into our home and looked after him as if she were his mother. He adored her and copied everything she did, making training so easy for me.

Harry was no sooner home when we discovered I was expecting our first child. James was born eight months later. Both Purdey and Harry were totally accepting of him and we were suddenly a family of five. James's first ever word was Purdey and he would giggle and squeal whenever he saw the dogs.

Sadly this was not to continue as we lost Purdey through kidney failure when she was just eleven years old. We were heartbroken. Luckily James was only one so he didn't understand, just seemed confused when he'd call for her and no one came. My husband and I were too upset to consider getting another dog. We felt she couldn't be replaced and that was that. However, we hadn't considered what might happen to Harry.

He was two years old by this time and had been the happiest and healthiest dog. Suddenly he became lethargic, sad, biting at his paws till they bled, always poorly and at the vet. We felt that he missed Purdey so much that he was suffering from depression. Our solution; another puppy.

I heard that there was a litter of six available near Brighton, so we went to have a look, taking James with us. He was excited seeing so many puppies running around. We chose another girl this time, as we felt that the boy/girl combination had worked so well for us before. Soon we were bringing home *Forestland Painted Lady*, who we called Emma.

We now had a very young family – Harry, 2, James, 1 and puppy, Emma. Harry and Emma bonded completely. He reverted to his old self and she loved him to bits, following him everywhere and pulling him around by his ears, which he always allowed her to do. James adored them both and they all grew up together having many happy years.

When Harry was eleven, he was diagnosed with chronic gall bladder and liver problems. He was medicated and things were okay for a while but we had to say goodbye just a couple of weeks before his thirteenth birthday. Again we were heartbroken, but this time had to deal with James's sadness too. He'd never suffered a loss like this before in his young life.

Emma handled things well. She'd watched Harry deteriorate and by the last weeks of his life, was leaving him alone more, not expecting him to play. We feel that she knew how ill he was and that he was nearing the end. We gave her all our attention and love and that seemed to be enough for her.

We thought about getting another puppy, but by then Emma was eleven so we decided against it.

Above: Joey (right) and Chloe (left)

A year later she developed a lump on her face that turned out to be cancerous. We took her to the Fitzpatrick hospital in Guildford, but the prognosis wasn't good and they gave her just a few months to live.

Emma was a fighter and it was nearly a year later when we had to say goodbye to her. It was so sad watching the tumour grow. Shelties have such beautiful faces and to watch hers become so disfigured on one side was heart-breaking. Finally, it burst and that was the end. All three of us took her to the vet and were with her for her last breath.

We came home to an empty house; with no dogs for the first time in 24 years.

That was in December 2019. As we all know, the world as we knew it, changed soon after that [due to the COVID-19 pandemic]. It took quite a while before we were able to get another puppy. We now have Joey who's nearly two and Chloe who's seven months but that's a story for another time…!

Clockwise from back left: Darcey, Tai, Ziggi, Indy. Owned by Tracey and Bernadette Baudains, photo by Carl King Photography.

A GIFT FROM ZEUS

Left: Zeus and right: Tara

My love of shelties began 36 years ago when I moved from Essex up to Suffolk. My boyfriend at the time was so fed up with me saying how much I missed my cat so he took me to see a friend of his in Newmarket. In the lounge, six fluffballs were playing together. He asked me which one I liked and I answered, 'how could anyone choose?!'

He insisted and the one I pointed to, he told me, was mine! We were at the home of Elaine Lawson, a well-known sheltie breeder at the time. Elaine was to become a very good friend of mine over the years – she was my "go-to" for anything sheltie.

Two weeks later we returned to collect Tara. She lived a happy, healthy life with us until she was 14 years old. When Tara was four years old, I was enchanted with this breed and wanted another puppy so with Elaine's help we tried to breed from Tara with the intention of keeping one of her pups.

However, all did not go well, as Tara was found to have a pyometra but the operation was fortunately successful. This scary experience taught me that in the future, I would have all my bitches spayed. I realised I did not want to be a breeder, just wanted the companionship and love that this beautiful breed brings.

Elaine did not have any pups for sale at that time, so we decided to look around for a "ready-made" playmate for Tara. We found one and I became the owner of two shelties.

Poppy was a sweetie, but so tiny. She had been the runt of a litter and was so sick for the first few months. She had trouble trying to keep food down and seemed to have a permanent upset tummy. We were back and forth to the vet with her many times and were constantly syringing water into her mouth to keep her hydrated.

Poppy

Tara was a star and knew her "sister" was not well. I felt guilty for giving up so much of my time to Poppy.

Poppy sadly passed away aged 9, having been diagnosed with Lupus at 7, and lived her last two years on steroids. So I was now able to lavish all my love on Tara for her last few years. I was devasted when she passed away at 14 due to kidney failure.

By that time, Elaine had moved away, and we had sadly lost touch. I scoured all the adverts for pups for sale and eventually ended up in Luton to pick up Pollyanna. She was an absolute beauty – born in the year 2000, I collected her on bonfire night in the pouring rain. She rode back in the car on my neighbour's lap.

When she was about three months old, I became worried. A couple of times she had leapt up from her bed when someone came to the door and screamed! On our short walk to the park, she had climbed up a small three-inch mound and fallen over.

I rushed to the vet who did several tests. They sent me to the Animal Health Trust and diagnosed her with double hip dysplasia. My heart was broken as I knew nothing about this.

Through my searching online, and my determination to make life better for her, I had her on many holistic supplements throughout her life. To add to her problems, she broke a cruciate ligament at nine years old chasing a pigeon in the garden. My vet suggested removing her hip ball at the same time and she then endured a long (caged) recovery period but coped with it all so well. I used to call her my little super-trooper!

She recovered well but sadly was unable to climb the stairs in my old house, so became an extension of my right arm for the rest of her life. I carried her up and down those stairs SO many times!

At 13, I had to make the dreadful decision to have her put to sleep. She had not eaten for about four days, despite being offered all kinds of her favourite foods. She was being sick and had already been diagnosed with kidney failure. I remember it well, it was a Monday morning and she had been sick all night. She just looked at me with her sad eyes, saying "come on Mum, it's my time to go".

Pollyanna

I woke up my partner, and said, come on, we are going to say goodbye to Polly. He leapt up from the bed with tears in his eyes and we all cuddled. We drove down to the vets and said goodbye to her, breaking our hearts. On the drive home, we passed Elaine's house (now with someone else living there and I cried out – "oh where is Elaine when I need her!"

Afterwards, the house was so miserable. I had not lived in this house without a sheltie! I cannot describe the gloominess and darkness in the house in the days following her death. We used to sit at night and cry to each other "we've got no shelties!" I knew I had to find another pup as soon as possible. However, I was very wary and did not want to end up with another with hip dysplasia or something worse.

Therefore, I went on the Kennel Club website and contacted six breeders, explaining our predicament, stating we were not breeders, just a lover of the breed who wanted a sheltie as a pet and part of our family. From those six emails, I only received one reply explaining that a friend named Elaine Wilson had a litter of puppies and gave me her landline number.

I rang her straight away and launched into introducing myself. She stopped me in mid-sentence and said "hello, Jan, it's Elaine here! Yes, I have a litter of pups, my first litter in ten years, you can take your pick!" Elaine had since remarried (hence the name change) and lived in Nottinghamshire.

I cannot describe my happiness in finding Elaine again and I will always be grateful for that one reply to my emails. I knew that a pup from Elaine would be healthy – she always had her bitches and sires hip-scored and eye tested. The pups were only born on 2nd January, so we would have to wait until they were six weeks old when we could go up and choose one and then go back to pick them up at eight weeks!

Cheeky Dice!

The time passed very slowly and in February we drove up to Elaine's to meet the pups. Only boys were available. I had never had a boy before, only bitches. We chose *Morestyle Black Ice* – or Dice as we decided to name him.

Luckily, I did not have to return to Nottinghamshire as Elaine was coming down to visit her daughter in the next village and offered to bring him down here to me. Wow! Was I lucky! Finding my friend again and having a pup delivered to my door! We loved Dice to pieces, but I have to say, he was the most destructive puppy I had ever had.

Elaine asked me to keep in touch with news on how he was developing and we used to keep in contact via Messenger. I told her how he chewed up all the furniture, ripped tissues, dug holes in the garden, chewed my carpets, emptied bins, chased lawnmowers, left teeth marks on my chair legs and more.

I had started taking him to a local dog training school each week in the hope to improve matters and I think I had shares in cans of anti-chew spray! We loved him to pieces, but I had never known a more mischievous, destructive puppy!

Eventually, Elaine suggested tentatively, adding to our family. A blue merle dog had become available from one of her friends as he was too large to breed from. At the end of March, Elaine arrived with her friend Janet Ambler and brought Zeus.

Zeus and Dice

Zeus was a few months older than Dice and a pure gentleman! Mild-mannered, gorgeous and would be a good example for Dice to follow. She left him here with me for a week, crying as she left. If I did not want to keep him, I could send him back with her the following week on her next visit to her daughter! What?! How could anyone want to give this beautiful sheltie back?! It was absolute love at first sight for me and Dice.

I did, at one stage wonder whether this was such a good idea, in that Dice might pass on some of his unfavourable tendencies to Zeus – but luckily this did not happen. Dice and Zeus in the following weeks became inseparable.

Zeus was such a charming little man. He followed me everywhere and became my shadow, my heart dog. Even now, writing about him brings me to tears. You could never in a million years ask for a better, well-behaved puppy. He taught little Dice well, he stopped digging holes in the garden and chewing my furniture and instead spent his energies on playing with Zeus at every opportunity. We all had such fun that year – we took them to the beach, days out with friends, visits to my Mum who adored both my boys.

Little did I know that year, that tragedy was about to strike. Just before Christmas, Zeus became unwell. He had a touch of gastroenteritis. I took him to my vet, who kept him in for the night on fluids and pain relief and also took x-rays in case he had swallowed something in the park.

He was released back to me and upon arriving back home, crept into his bed and stayed there.

Dice went mad when he got back and wanted to play, but Zeus seemed very sleepy, so we let him rest. He ate dinner that night with relish and things were looking up. I took them both out the next morning for a quiet walk in the park. Over the weekend he continued to improve, and I updated Elaine and Janet with the good news.

But on the Monday morning, he didn't seem quite as bouncy and had a slightly runny tum again, so I decided to take him back to my vet. My vet showed me the results of all his tests on his computer and suggested that they send him to a Referral Practice for a scan in case the x-rays had missed something.

They managed to get him in for an appointment at 11 am the next morning and asked me if I wanted them to keep him in overnight, as his temperature was slightly high. I stayed with him at the vet that evening and this is the last photo I took of him.

I told Elaine about Dice, being so miserable and not eating, and she suggested Seren, a pup of Janet's who was too big for showing and was bullying some other new pups. She sent me a photo – another blue merle. I looked at her and fell in love again. Elaine brought her down

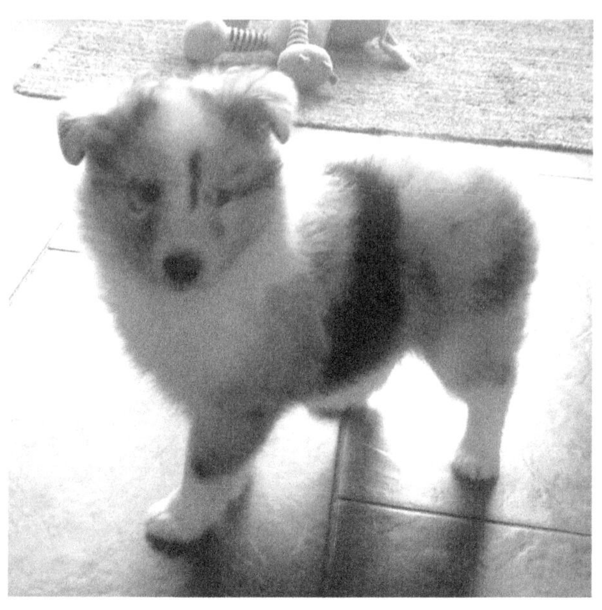

Left: my last photo of Zeus and right: Seren (now Pandora)

to me a few weeks later. Dice seemed to cheer up and started tentatively eating again. We renamed Seren to Pandora as the name means a gift from Zeus. Elaine brought her down to me under the same conditions as when she had brought Zeus. Dice started to come out of his shell (but even now, some nine years later, still sits in Zeus's chair on my back porch with a wistful look in his eyes).

The next day was Tuesday 17th December, one week before Christmas and I got a phone call from the Referral Practice at lunchtime to say my Zeus had died... he was only 2 and a half years old!

They could not give me a reason and offered to do a post-mortem free of charge to find out his cause of death. They said it would help other cases like this in the future. It filled me with horror, the thought of his beautiful body being taken apart. I wanted to remember him as he was but eventually agreed.

My poor little Dice was inconsolable – he wouldn't eat and on the advice of Elaine I got some Ignatia in the hope that might help him, but it didn't seem to make any difference. He wouldn't eat, didn't want to play and looked so forlorn. I thought I would lose him too!

I had sent several emails to the vet at the Referral Practice about Zeus's post-mortem but had not one reply. The office did call me to tell me his ashes were ready to collect and I drove down to pick them up on my own which, on reflection, was not a good idea.

Driving home with his box of ashes on the seat next to me, I broke my heart and could not see to drive through the tears. I spoke to him as if he were still alive, he loved driving in that car! I remember saying "oh my Zeus, I never thought your last drive in this car with me would be like this."

To finish Zeus' story, I did eventually get a three-paragraph email from the Referral Practice saying that the post-mortem had been inconclusive, and they could give no reason for his death. They withheld pictures from the actual post-mortem as they "did not want to upset me with pictures of his internal organs".

When I took Pandora to the vet for her first lot of jabs, I asked my own vet, what they thought of Zeus's post-mortem results. He told me they have been "unprofessional", and had lied to me – I looked at him totally thunderstruck. I don't think he realised I had not seen the actual post-mortem, but just had a short email.

It would seem that instead of doing a scan, they had plunged a needle into a main artery and he had bled to death on the table. I felt I had to do something, for the memory of my Zeus. I knew it would not bring him back, but decided I would take the case to the Royal College of Veterinary Surgeons, which I did. The case got to the third stage, exactly one year after his death but then was unfortunately thrown out.

Pandora will be eight years old in November (we call her Panda for short). She is a gorgeous girl and a total bull in a china shop. Dice, who will be ten in January – now has his new friend. She is his niece and although it's not the same relationship he had with Zeus, I think they love each other!

Photos and story by Janet Savill

THE PAWPRINTS ON YOUR HEART

Here's to those very first and special Shelties in our lives that have started the lifelong love affair with this wonderful breed

"

Bonnie was my first Sheltie in 1970. My parents made a condition that I be responsible and take her to training classes. That was the start to my many years competing and being owned by Shelties.

Louise Saunders from Perthshire, Scotland

"

Lizzie became very sick suddenly and we had to make the heartbreaking decision to put her down. She was only nine years young. I was devastated and still am every time I look at her pictures. She was, as all shelties are, devoted, sensitive, loving, funny and smart. She gave me unconditional love and I miss her every day

Bobbie Franco, Maryland, USA

"

I had always thought there was something special about shelties and had always admired them from afar but it wasn't until 2020 that I finally convinced my other half to get a dog.

The best thing we ever did was bring Riley into our lives. He will be three years old in December and he is our world. There is nothing I wouldn't do for our amazing boy and I couldn't be more certain we chose the right breed, there's nothing quite like a sheltie!

Charlotte Dable from Leicestershire, UK

THE PAWPRINTS ON YOUR HEART

" My first sheltie was a tri male called Marlee. We had Marlee from a puppy and he was such a character. He was a clever little dog, was easy to train but did most things without being taught.

One day I was fetching washing in from the tumble dryer (kept in a shed) and I dropped a sock. Just as a joke I said, "Oh go and pick that up Marlee," I was so surprised that he did! After that he would pick things up for me which I dropped. He would put things in the washing machine and get my slippers when I walked into the house. He wouldn't stop barking until I put them on.

He loved visitors to the house and he would fetch anything he could get his teeth on and take it to them to play fetch. He loved ball games, bringing the ball straight back to me and be sitting ready for the next throw.

At bedtimes he would know when the time was and would be upstairs before me. He did this so that he would not be left downstairs alone. He crossed the Rainbow Bridge at age 15 years and 10 days and took my heart with him.

Vick Harbour from Peterborough, UK

"

This is my handsome Harry, *Licosateria Miri Star*. He is a bit of a diva, loves being the centre of attention and is a very competitive, confident boss of three collies at home.

He loves agility and is super fast. Before Covid he had won up to Grade 5 although he could get higher if his owner ran faster! He has also done a little bit of dog dancing, shows off beautifully and has lots of tricks up his sleeve. But mainly he's just in it for the food, well, he is a sheltie after all but I wouldn't be without him!

Sonia from the UK

"

For many years, my dream has always been to acquire a Shetland Sheepdog one day. This dream came true on 4th September, 2021 with the arrival of Shanel, a little blue merle.

Shanel is an extremely sweet, affectionate, sporty and very cheerful little dog. She is a daily happiness and loves walks.

One of her particularities is her very elegant gait worthy of a dancer.

On the other hand, she has her very rustic and a bit brusque side, from her well marked atavism, instead of catching the sheep, she bites the calves!

Shanel is a dream come true.

Coline Van Amerongen from Le Thor, France

THE PAWPRINTS ON YOUR HEART

"

Milly, 9 is an Australian Champion - C*H Peerielee Colours Of The Wind*. Milly is my very first Shetland Sheepdog. She is my first show dog, my first dog to title all by myself in the show ring and my first velcro dog. She is my heart and soul and I would be absolutely lost without her.
Milly loves nothing more than simply being by my side and looking absolutely fabulous doing so!

Allison Begnell from Jimboomba, Australia

"

Freya is my little ray of sunshine and gives my life a whole new meaning. We're always going on adventures, rain or shine, with camera in hand, playing fetch or snuggling. She brings so much joy to everyone's life, that I've forgotten how to be sad when she's around. I can't wait for many more years with my best girl.

Sarah Andrews from Kent, UK

Lassie and Ben are very precious members of our family. After Trevor had a stroke two years ago, Lassie and Ben would visit him in hospital. Lassie would cuddle as close to Trevor as possible and hated when she had to go home without him.

When Trevor came home, Lassie wouldn't leave his side. Trevor is a lot better these days and Lassie and Ben are enjoying their walks and living their best life going to fun shows. I haven't been well with Covid but the dogs always keep me going. We love Lassie and Ben more than words can say.

Pauline and Trevor Buxton from Aberdeenshire, Scotland, UK

"

When I decided to get a puppy in 2020, there was no question, it had to be a sheltie. Having had three beautiful shelties in the family previously, I knew how sweet, loving and cheeky they were, and wow, my Bonnie did not disappoint! The amount of joy and love she has brought in to my family and my life is unbelievable. She takes us on adventures, days out and holidays. Our walkies everyday bring smiles to the faces of the people we pass. One of my favourite traits of hers is how friendly she is. Everyone, even strangers, get a big, bum-waggling welcome. Never change Bonnie, my sweet, happy girl.

My Gran and Uncle's dog Dusty who is now over the Rainbow Bridge is never far from my mind and always will hold a special place in my heart. We lost him at fourteen and a half in Summer 2016. He was my forever puppy, full of mischief and love. This photo was taken at Dornoch Beach where he enjoyed many family holidays.

Nicolla Martin from Perth, UK

"

This is Fizz, she is 13 years old and my first dog. She's the sweetest soul and loves everyone she meets. She is a sassy girl who knows she is gorgeous. Fizz is the most wonderful dog, she is one of a kind, and I don't know where I'd be without her.

Phoebe Fillery from Kent, UK

THE PAWPRINTS ON YOUR HEART

"

I was very fortunate when Lady came into my life. She was heaven sent. My life changed and our home was alive again with this furry blue merle little girl. She is so good and quiet and leaps around frantically when she knows we are going walkies. She is such a friendly little girl. She has brought our lives much joy again.

Lady is so smart and knows our routine so well. She is the reason I get up in the mornings and I feel that she has trained me and not the other way round. I love her to bits and the house would be so empty without her.

Vicky Harbour from Peterborough, UK

"

On 5th July 2022, I dressed Quinn, 6 and Maisie,18 weeks in their festive red, white and blue scarf to take them to my hometown Fourth of July parade which I have attended most every year of my life. Maisie wasn't feeling well so we decided to stay back. Suddenly, we heard a series of gunfire shots and many sirens immediately ring out. We knew something wasn't right.

There had been a mass shooting with seven people killed and hundreds injured. This small quant city on the North Shore Chicago will remain forever changed.

In the days after the shooting the people mourned the loss of lives, innocence and of freedom on a day meant to celebrate the opposite! But thanks to Quinn and Maisie I am able to cope and get some comfort and joy from what would otherwise have been one of the darkest times.

Jan Anne Dubin, Illinois, USA

"I grew up with shelties in the family so it was no surprise that when I decided to get my very own dog, it would be a sheltie. In addition to being the most faithful companion, Daisy has introduced me to the wonderful world of dog activities and sports. Together we have learned about and competed in agility, obedience, rally and scent work, and she took me to Crufts as part of the Sheltie Superstars Obreedience team which was beyond my wildest dreams!

However, the best thing about Daisy is that she is also my best friend, knowing when I am not feeling great and licking away my tears when I am sad. She was with me when I broke my hip, looking after me and encouraging me to get back on my feet and out there again with her. She even pulls my socks off for me! Strangely we often share the same illnesses and go through our treatments together, some very serious. But we have so much fun together and as she loves everyone, I have been able to take her everywhere with me including lots of trips in the campervan and visiting friends.

Daisy has now pretty much retired but is still a little monkey. She has had to put up with the addition of young Zorro to our sheltie family which she does with grace and he adores her. In her senior years, she has perfected the art of stealing treats and barking!

Callie Mather, Bath, UK

SUPER SMART SHELTIES

Shelties are intelligent, love being active and having a job to do. Here some of our readers shared some photos and stories about the activities they do together!

Zorro, 4 is on a mission! To sniff in as many different venues as possible. So far he has searched in a stableyard, football ground, aviation hangar with real planes, railway stations, disused warehouse, equestrian centre, village hall, farm and magistrates court. He loves his scentwork!

But that is just for fun. He is also working his way through the Scentwork UK trials, currently working at Level 5 and will continue to compete in DDT (Detection Dog Trials) which are more environmental.

Zorro also loves dancing and doing tricks so we are exploring the world of Heelwork to Music which is fascinating and certainly a challenge!

Photos courtesy of Rebecca Reed Photography

Above: Sheltie Superstars Obreedience Team Crufts 2019. Team: Callie Mather & Daisy, Angela Rowe & Buddy, Rowena Steady & Toes, Vanessa Hardin & Tutti Fruitti, Jean Tuck & Zac. Right: Callie & Daisy at Crufts 2019. Below right: Daisy with International Rally Rosette on Podium!

Daisy, 11 from Bath, UK has had a highly active and competitive life. She has competed in agility, obedience, rally and scent work. Daisy and her owner even went to Crufts as part of the Sheltie Superstars Obreedience team!

Daisy's owner, Callie says:

"Obreedience is a team event where four dogs of the same breed and their handlers walk in a synchronised heelwork pattern together, then each dog performs an individual exercise chosen from one of the following: stop the dog and play, send to bed, retrieve own scent article, and retrieve. During the heats, Daisy tried out all four exercises but at Crufts, she did "stop the dog". In 2019 the Sheltie Superstars qualified for Crufts and came 4th. Due to bad health during the heats leading up to 2020 Crufts, Daisy did not take part in so many heats so was reserve for the team who went on to win the competition that year, but she was there to support them!

Daisy has also competed in rally and reached level 4 Ex before lockdown hit. She went on to qualify at level 6 Ex in Rally Online. However, her big claim to fame in rally was to be in a UK team entered into the first ever Virtual International Rally Competition. This was run

by CSEN from Italy and the UK team was delighted to be placed first.

Another online achievement was to be part of the Black and Gold Team in the Allbreedience Virtual competition where after three heats the team came overall second out of 50 teams internationally. Our team consisted of Hap Happel's lovely sheltie, Gigi, a border collie and a golden retriever.

Daisy also loves sniffing and has enjoyed scent work for fun as well as working her way up the Scentwork UK trials currently working at Level 4. She is such a versatile little dog and has even dabbled online with some heelwork to music!"

SUPER SMART SHELTIES

Finn, 4 loves his Rally-O and scentwork in Dunedin, New Zealand

Daisy, 11 from Bath, UK

Badger, 1, showing off his trick, from Cambridgeshire UK

Wavesong Jumping Jac Flash competing for Team GB. He has four world medals and loves the green carpet!

Laddie, 1 competing in Rally-O from Dunedin, New Zealand

Aline from Budapest, Hungary

Breccan, 5 from Ohio, USA

RICHMAUS LINEAGE

A group of our regular contributors to the annual surprisingly come from the same litter so we decided to track down some more photos from the Richmaus kennel–you can certainly see where they get their good genes from!

Right: IR CH Irish Legend of Naverrem and Richmaus Picture Perfect, parents of Teddy, Naverrem Mr Sitges at Richmaus IKC (below).

Naverrem Mr Sitges at Richmaus x Richmaus Red Bow produced a litter of nine in 2018 – here are four of them! Far left: Richmaus Yogi 'Teddy', top middle: Richmaus Chewbacca 'Teddy-Boo', above: Richmaus Goldilocks 'Rosie' and left: Richmaus Primrose 'Joy'.

Left: Breeder Maureen with Richmaus Star, 'Freya' and above: Richmaus Royal Romance, 'Gilly' as a puppy

SWIMMING FOR LIFE

No one suspected anything was wrong with Abby as a puppy but the occasional limp after playing turned out to be a much bigger issue.

I picked up Abby and her littermate brother, Tanner in September 2019. They were eight weeks old and the sweetest puppies. I got littermates because I lost a sheltie and a border collie within three months of each other between January and March 2019. They were both over 13 years old and it left my Blaze all alone, he was so sad.

But as soon as the puppies walked in the door, he was a different dog! He was so happy and looked after his little brother and sister 24/7. He really loved them. Blaze was rescued in 2016 at four years old. His DNA said he was 50% sheltie, 25% collie and 25% aussie and I can see all of those breeds when I look at him.

As you know, puppies play and jump on each other! Tanner always picked on his sister Abby. The first time I can remember Abby limping was when Tanner jumped on her and knocked her down while playing. I took her to the vet and they gave her Novox.

Within a few days, she was fine and because she recovered, they did not feel a need to do X-rays. This continued to happen over the next year and a half and Abby always recovered. In April 2022, Abby started limping again and I did not know what caused it this time but I gave her Novox as I had done in the past. But this time, the limping did not go away so, after two weeks, I took her to the vet.

X-rays showed bilateral elbow dysplasia which was worse on the front left leg. The vet determined this was congenital and was not caused by any injury. She was simply born this way and as she grew, the separation in the elbow joint worsened. At almost three years old, it was finally showing the effects of the elbow separation. Abby was referred to an orthopaedic surgical specialist, Dr Anna Aman, at Veterinary Referral and Critical Care in Richmond, Virginia (VRCC).

After seeing Dr Anna Aman, I was told that nothing could be done surgically. Had we caught it before she was 18 months old, they could have done something surgically, but now, it was too late. I realized then that I should have requested X-rays the first time Abby limped because we would have discovered the congenital defect. I am sharing this story so that other Sheltie owners can learn from our experience. If you have limping at a very early age (before 18 months), request X-rays.

Instead of surgery, Dr Aman suggested a variety of interventions to help Abby. They were:

- To lose weight to lessen the stress on her joints.
- Avoid high-impact activities like running and jumping.
- Add joint supplements such as Fish Oil.
- Omega-3 fatty acid and Cosequin for long-term use.
- Continue the Novox and add Adequan injections. Adequan is a polysulfated glycosaminoglycan (made from bovine tracheal cartilage). Novox will be stopped if these other interventions work because long-term use of NSAIDs can be detrimental to a dog's health.
- Do physical therapy/rehabilitation in the swimming pool and add laser therapy.
- Consider Stem Cell Therapy and Platelet Rich Plasma (PRP). Recent studies have shown decreased pain and lameness, as well as increased range of motion and mobility in patients treated with stem cells and PRP.

Making Progress

So far, Abby has lost four pounds in four weeks and we plan to continue until she loses ten pounds. We will continue this diet until she is at the ideal weight recommended by Dr Aman.

She is swimming with a veterinary physical therapist two times a week. We also have a swimming pool at our home so she swims at home an additional 1-2 times a week.

She has also completed the first three weeks of Adequan injections and now gets injections monthly.

Our regular vet recommended we use an Assisi Loop. It uses targeted pulsed electromagnetic field technology (PEMF). It is a safe, FDA-cleared, drug-free therapy for treating pain and inflammation. We purchased one and use it daily. We love being able to do this in the convenience of our home. We have added Fish Oil and Turmeric supplements to her diet and after Abby has lost ten pounds, we will see Dr Aman again to determine if we will do the Stem Cell Therapy and PRP.

We have been very pleased with these interventions. Abby is not limping much at all and really enjoys swimming. Swimming will become her main exercise in the summer in our pool. In the winter, we will use our local veterinary aquatic centre and we will provide an additional update on her progress in the 2024 *I Love Shelties Annual*!

Photos and story by Chris Meade, Virginia, USA

Freya, 2 from Kent,, UK

Fun On The Farm!

Greetings from baby Apricot!

Apricot is three years old and sends love from her farmhouse located in Mariager, Denmark!

She is living her best life, playing together with her mom Mille and the rest of the gang. This year our gang expanded with 5 chickens and 8 ducks! How exciting! Shortly after we got our feathered friends, they started sitting on eggs and suddenly we have 17 chickens and 11 ducks.

Baby Apricot loves her ducks and chickens, and especially the delicious eggs they leave just laying around. That's how Apricot gets in trouble, she steals eggs and she acts surprised when I ask her where all the eggs have gone?

Fabrication Française

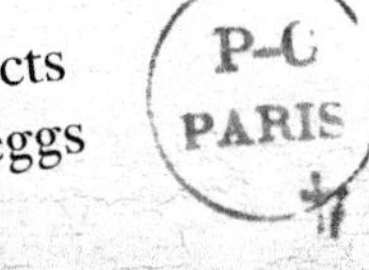

Another thing is the wonderful long walks together with daddy. The "sick paw" from where it was broken at eleven weeks old is working so well and Apricot has no more pain. Farm life suits Apricot so much, she really loves it and its very beneficial to her mental health, making her calm and even more loving.

This December something very exciting is going to happen! Apricot's mum and dad are heading to Florida, USA to celebrate the wedding of Emma's mum (see page 50). When Apricot broke her leg, her mum became close facebook friends with Emma's mum Barbara, writing to each other daily. Isn't it wonderful how shelties connect people across the world?

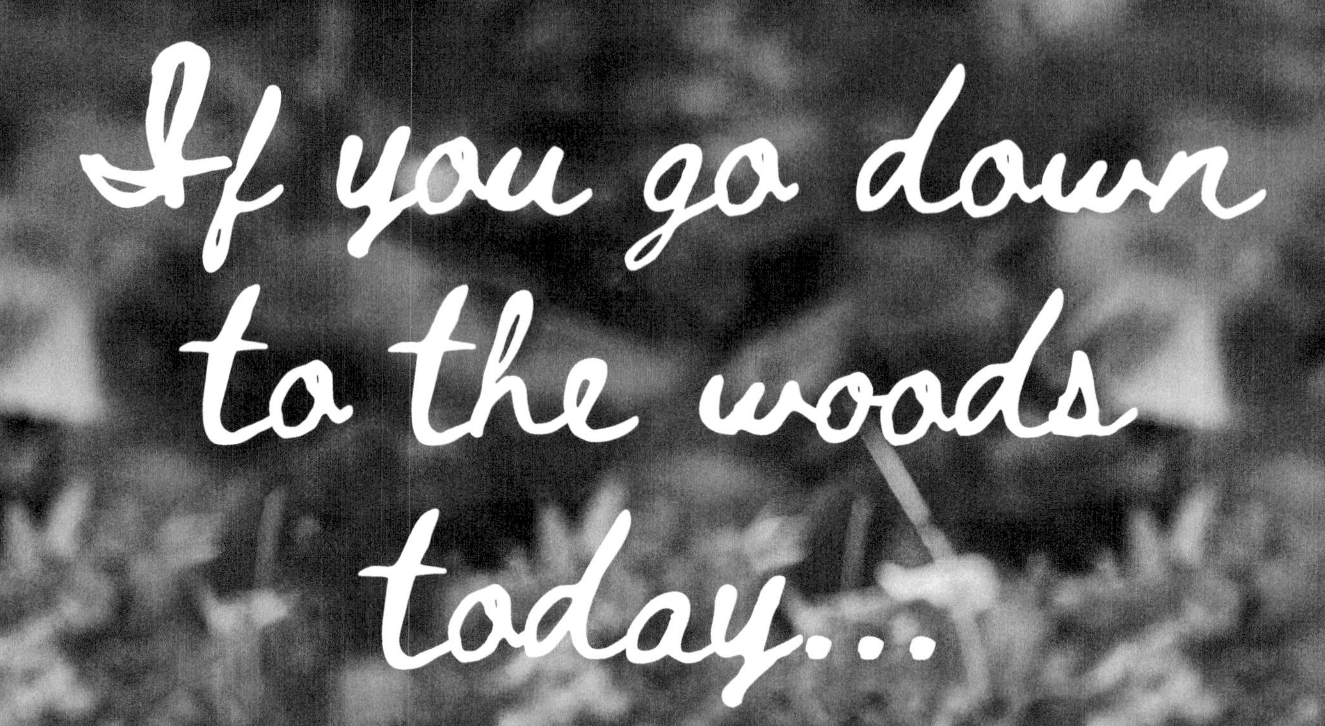

If you go down to the woods today...

Teddy and his cousins Mia and Talia (aka Shelties By The Sea) went for what they thought was a normal walk in the woods when they stumbled upon something very unexpected...

To the
Teddy
Bear's
Picnic

It started off as a normal walk in the woods until...

'Come quick and see!' said Mr Rabbit.

'What's going on?' Mia asked confused.

'Look, the foxes are going this way!' said Talia.

'You don't want to miss this!' said the squirrel.

'Miss what? What is happening?'

Teddy asked the owl and the mouse but everyone was too excited to answer.

The teddy bears are having a picnic!

'Don't worry,' said Mia.
'I'm the oldest, I'll check it out and see if it's safe!'

'It's alright,the teddy bears are just having a picnic!' said Mia.

'Can we join them?' asked Talia.

'Yes, please say we can stay!' said Teddy.

Pooh

'Cheese and sausages, oh woof!'

'Don't touch Paddington's marmalade sandwich!'

'Can I have some honey please, Pooh bear?'

'When can we have another picnic?'

Pooh

HUBBLE'S HAPPY RETIREMENT

After an active life travelling and training, Hubble is making the most of her golden years

Photos and story by Wendy Lee from Warwickshire, UK.

My golden oldie is now 14 years old and is enjoying her retirement. Hubble has achieved her Good Citizen awards from the Kennel Club. She trained in Agility, Rally O, Heelwork to Music and Tricks UK achieving over 70 tricks.

She participated in activity dogs at Crufts three years running and at the English Shetland Sheepdog Club Centenary gathering at Stoneleigh where she represented Heelwork to Music as well as auditioning for a TV programme.

Freestyle Heelwork to Music was her favourite discipline and she often had the habit of slipping in a new move in the routine when in competition that fitted in well with the music and overall routine. Thankfully, she knew best and I loved the fact that she enjoyed it as much as I did.

Hubble can be taken anywhere that she is allowed to go and is a credit to me. She has been camping, caravanning, and now in a motorhome. She has enjoyed a holiday on a narrow boat, travels on buses, trains and ferries.

When we go away she is calm, friendly and impeccably behaved. She has made people stop and talk to her, even offering money to buy her! Even those that don't like dogs seem to like her.

At dog clubs or in a controlled environment she has been used with reactive dogs to provide them with confidence. She has been bought up with rabbits, guinea pigs and a cat and has respected them all.

Her favourite day out is to visit the beach. She used to love the kids running in and out and along the water's edge, not barking once at them.

Her shining star though has been being my 'hearing dog'. I have profound hearing loss that has become worse over the years. I wear hearing aids but still miss things. Hubble naturally and instinctively supported me and often used her paws and eyes to attract my attention to what she has heard and then touch me. I used a clicker to teach her 'touch' which she began to use to get my attention instead.

In later years she could tell the cars of our adult kids before they left home, as well as my husband's and mine and even the Morrisons delivery van!

I taught her to pick her lead up when she is attached to it, to pick up anything I may drop out of a pocket, help bring washing to the machine, pull clothes off lower rungs of the clothes horse and even pull socks off. She was a willing participant, always eager to please and would use her initiative too. I asked Hearing Dogs for the Deaf if they could assess her and provide accreditation but was told no as they hadn't trained her.

We have an understanding between us where we know what each other wants without gestures or commands. It is a very special bond indeed and I feel so blessed to have such a special dog.

She now lives alone having sadly lost our beloved cat of 21.5 years of age in February. She comes to life when she meets up with other family members' dogs –her playfulness emerges. Occasionally, she will go into a play bow and dance around a bit and is more motivated to walk further when she's with her dog friends.

Hubble still enjoys holidays in the motorhome and continues to be admired by all who meet her. She doesn't look her age at all but acts it by being slower and sleeps a lot. However, she still knows her routine and when it's mealtime!

Hubble has now gone deaf herself so the Makaton signs she has learnt have come in handy as well as gesturing and of course the eye contact between us. I miss her 'help' a lot as our roles have changed but she still enjoys living life to the full.

Sophie Parkhill is the multi award winning artist behind *SP Wildlife Art.*

This pastel painting was created for a client of their beautiful Sheltie called Smudge. Since Sophie had two paintings featured in last years book, she wanted to share this painting too!

To commission a portrait of your fluffy friends, contact Sophie via email at spwildlifeartist@hotmail.com or via her website www.spwildlifeart.com

You can also follow updates of Sophies pet portraits and wildlife creations on Instagram and Facebook @SPWildlifeArt.

Rainbow Bridge

These are always the hardest pages to put together but it is a privilege to be able to honour these special souls that have crossed over to rainbow bridge. Until we meet again sweet shelties, run happy, run free.

We picked up Anya (Andy Pandy) from the rescue centre at just 18 weeks old, unwanted due to having a heart murmur. She joined our other four shelties and her murmur was never a problem.

She was our 13th sheltie and we were so lucky to have her in our lives. She earned her KCGC Gold award, did agility, won many companion shows, loved the beach, meeting people but most importantly, she was (and still is) my heart dog, my best friend.

Sadly, aged just over 8 years old she became unwell, was diagnosed with lymphoma and crossed over Rainbow Bridge at 8 years, 10 months. She's left us with wonderful memories and is missed and thought of every day.

Sandra Hime, Carmarthen, UK

Amazingly, when we adopted Teddy at eight weeks of age, he was already trained to use a kitty litter box so we didn't have to take him outside in the frigid Minnesota winter for a few weeks. He was always so happy and loved meeting people and giving kisses. Because of his loving personality, people gravitated toward him and frequently called him "the people's dog". Our fur-son crossed the Rainbow Bridge on May 14th at 12.5 years of age. He is greatly missed and will forever be in our hearts.

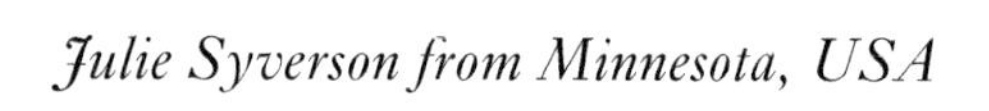

Julie Syverson from Minnesota, USA

Tuppence, *Dark Honey CDex UDex*
22.12.93 – 13.1.2011

Sire: *Ch. Herds the Helmsman*
Dam: *Dippersmoor Dorina*

It was a privilege and a pleasure to own Tuppence. She had a gorgeous temperament with no fear and was everybody's friend.

Tuppence had quite a unique lifetime spanning 17 years and winning in four different disciplines. As a puppy, she was placed well in the breed ring, including several Best Puppy Awards. Then she went on to win in obedience at companion dog shows, agility and Championship Working Trials where she obtained the qualifications CDex (Companion Dog Excellent) and UDex (Utility Dog Excellent).

The UD qualification includes nose work, (tracking and searching), control exercises and agility (covering three jumps, scale 4ft. high, long jump 6ft, and clear jump 2 ft.) They have to obtain a percentage of points in each section to qualify. For some years Tuppence was the only Sheltie with the UDex qualification and her first UDex qualification was at Lauder where her track took her over four difficult terrains and she came 2nd. She won the Lonicera Shield for Working Trials for several years.

As well as her show career, she loved children and was quite happy to be handled by any child. She invariably won in children's handling classes and often won prettiest bitch and best trick. She was a favourite with the crowd when she took part in demonstrations of obedience and agility at various places and always succeeded with her party trick of retrieving a raw egg without breaking it. Regular visits were also made to rest homes where she was such a favourite with the elderly, at churches and schools demonstrating to the children. She also took part in the Christian Aid Walk every year (12 miles). During her last year, she was still winning veteran classes as she kept very agile and fit.

At home Tuppence had two German Shepherd companions, I think she sometimes thought she was a German Shepherd, (anything they can do, I can do better!) and until she was 16.5 years, she was still going on long walks with them.

Tuppence is so sadly missed but her memory will live on with so many people as she was well known and such a character. I thank God for her life and for the joy and companionship she has given me for 17 years. Farewell Tuppence. We will meet again someday.

Rosemary Turner, Dorset, UK

Rainbow Bridge

Ziggie, Sept 2010 - July 2022

Words cannot express the loss and sorrow and the huge gap left in my life now that my gorgeous, amazing little man has passed over the rainbow bridge. An extra bright star will forever shine in the night sky.

Ziggie was great at everything he did, reaching Grade 7 in Agility and getting into the final of Dogs In Need with me running first that day. I will always be so proud of you. You were such a happy, smiling little man who loved to work and play. So many memories that I will treasure forever.

My life will never be the same again without my beloved Ziggie by my side, but rest in peace my precious little man.

Linda Kightley, Norfolk, UK

Our best boy Flash passed away on the 20th of March 2021 at 14 years old.

He was a very special little guy who helped me through my many medical dramas. He allowed me unconditional cuddles when I was deeply distressed and felt like quitting life. He was beautiful, loving and an absolutely amazing boy that was loved by everyone who met him. I had a tattoo done in his memory as no matter what goes on he will never be forgotten

Ingrid Williamson, Shetland, UK

Blossom was born in South Korea on 6th April 2006. She then travelled to Malaysia and I met her in February 2012, just two weeks after she had given birth to five beautiful little girls.

I chose two of her pups; Enya and Glory and then Blossom also came to live with us. Finally, their half-sister Gracie joined us too. Blossom was such a sweetheart, always happy and she loved to play with the pups.

In 2014, Blossom once again travelled on a plane from Malaysia to England and soon adjusted to cooler temperatures. She loved to sunbathe and spent lots of time in the garden. In 2020, she was diagnosed with Canine Cognitive Dementia and it was heartbreaking to see her health decline.

Finally, on 5th November 2021, we had to say goodbye. Gracie adored Blossom and stayed by her side until the end. We miss her every day, she was a very special sheltie and will never be forgotten

Anneliese Brown, Lincolnshire, UK

Our sweet little girl Tansy went over the Rainbow Bridge on 23 March 2022. She suddenly developed a brain infection and although the vet at Dick White Referrals tried all they could to save her it wasn't to be. With breaking hearts we said goodbye to our girl in a very special, tender and loving way. Lady (Tansy's mother) misses her very much but we make sure she is given plenty of attention.

Tansy was such a good girl, loved her walks in the park and would cuddle up to Lady at night in the same bed, although she had her own. She was a sweet girl and looked at you with such innocence with her one blue eye and one brown.
Run free our sweet girl. We miss you very much.

Vicky Harbour, Peterborough, UK

LOOKS LIKE BUTTER WOULDN'T MELT!

Find out in next year's I Love Shelties Annual how this adorable little pup got to be called Tallywag!

STAY CONNECTED!

We hope you've enjoyed the annual and we look forward to sharing more stories and photos from the sheltie community next year. Thank you to everyone that sent in photos and stories – we couldn't make this book without you. If you'd like to keep up to date with our new projects and find out when submissions open for the *I Love Shelties Annual 2024*, sign up to our newsletter:

www.iloveshelties.com/newsletter

In the meantime, let us know what you thought of the book by leaving a review on Amazon and send us your photos of your pups enjoying their copy, we love to see your photos!

If you'd like to support us in the creation of this annual, you can now make a donation at **https://ko-fi.com/iloveshelties**

We'd love to invite you to our *I Love Shelties* community on *Mighty Networks* to connect with other sheltie lovers around the world.

To join please visit **www.iloveshelties.com/connect**

Follow I Love Shelties: www.facebook.com/ilovesheltiesworldwide

Email us at: hello@iloveshelties.com

Printed in Great Britain
by Amazon

11863953R00093